INNER WISDOM

The Challenge of Contextual Healing

Dean Black

TAPESTRY PRESS

Springville • Utah

DESIGN / RICHARD SUTTER

ISBN 0-929283-19-8 : $16.95. ISBN 0-92983-08-2 (pbk) : $9.95

Manufactured in the United States of America

I gratefully acknowledge the contributions of my associate Lyle Fletcher, whose editing skills and genius for finding just the right supporting quotes have greatly enriched this book.

Contents

To my wife, Claudia, who encourages
me often and supports me in
countless ways.

Introduction

For centuries now, two different kinds of healers have contended for the health-care market. Today we might call them "natural healers" and "medical doctors." In general, natural healers seek to *sustain* the body's natural processes, while medical doctors seek to *replace* them with drugs or machines. The two kinds of healers represent two distinct healing philosophies, or models, each with its own premises, its own healing principles, and its own methods for discovering truth.

For many of those centuries, the two healing models swung back and forth like a pendulum, as if each were correcting in turn the failures and limitations of the other.[1] Two or three centuries ago, the swinging began to get lopsided, and in the beginning years of this century it stopped altogether, firmly fixed on one of the two poles. The uncertainty, it seemed, had been resolved. One of the two models had been proven scientifically superior to the other. Medical therapies, it appeared, were valid. Natural therapies were not.

But the natural therapies refused to die. Natural healers persisted in plying their trade, as their clients

just as persistently sought to be plied upon. Since philosophic and scientific assaults had failed to daunt the
natural healers, medical authorities began working to
restrain them by legal means. On the whole, they have
succeeded rather well.

Medical authorities justify these legal restraints against
their competitors on the premise that they are protect-
ing consumers from fraud. Consumers, they argue, are
incapable of discerning the truth in an area so complex
as health. Over the past several decades, legal constraints against natural therapies have proven so successful that medicine now holds a practical monopoly in our
health-care market. Natural healers continue to operate,
but under oppressive and burdensome laws.

My own interest in these issues began when a natural
therapy—Chinese healing herbs—remedied allergies that
had plagued me all my life. I inquired into the philosophy behind the herbs and discovered a world of odd
concepts like *yin* and *yang*, the idea that health is a balance
of some sort, and the assertion that a natural healing
power exists, which the Chinese call *Chi*. I then perused
other natural healing principles and found the same
concepts in them, though obviously with different names.

My interest in writing this book began when I studied
a new kind of science that is most often called "chaos
theory," though it goes by other names as well. Unlike
the classical science of Francis Bacon, René Descartes,
and Isaac Newton (which undergirds modern medicine), chaos theory deals with patterns rather than parts.
And as I studied chaos theory, I began to notice curious
parallels between the principles of chaos theory and the
explanations of the old-time natural healers. To explain
how nature sustains her patterns, chaos theory uses
scientific concepts that sound very much like the sorts of
unscientific things natural healers say.

The more I studied these curious parallels, the more of them I saw. And I began to suspect something. What if natural healers have been noticing *intuitively* dimensions of nature that chaos theory is only now beginning to explain? If that's the case, the efforts to suppress natural healing on scientific grounds have surely been ill founded and unjust.

I'm persuaded now that this is indeed the case. Medicine's domination has been supported by philosophic and scientific premises that chaos theory now shows to be mistaken. Based on those mistaken premises, natural therapies have been unjustly suppressed, which has produced in our nation a grossly imbalanced health-care system that is now beginning to break down.

This is the theme I develop in this book. Although I explain some of the concepts of chaos theory, they really amount (as you'll see) to little more than common sense. Their essence is that a single system (a human body, for example) can behave in many different ways, depending on how it interacts with its *context*, or its surroundings. Applied to our health, this presents the possibility that, by adjusting how we relate to *our* context, we may adjust how our body behaves.

Beginning with this possibility, I discovered what seemed to me compelling evidence that cancer is contextual (due, that is, to our interaction with our context), and that other chronic illnesses may be contextual as well. If that's the case, restoring a healthy context should heal them, and fighting them with drugs would be misdirected at best, harmful or fatal at worst. This "context adjusting" is what natural healers have always claimed to do, and it is the premise that chaos theory now seems to sustain.

Because of this contextual emphasis, I no longer speak of natural healing, but of *contextual healing*. And for the same reason, I prefer not to talk of chaos theory, but of *contextual science*. Renaming things is risky and more than a bit presumptuous, but I wanted to use names that put the focus where it belongs—on the *context* of systems, not on their molecular details. So this book is about *contextual healing* (sometimes called "natural healing") as supported and sustained by the principles and methods of *contextual science*—or chaos theory as it is otherwise known.

The book is also about medicine's essential *incompleteness*. By focusing on medicine's incompleteness, I don't intend to minimize its successes, only to argue (1) that they have generally been limited to very specific kinds of emergencylike circumstances and (2) that medicine's success in those emergencylike circumstances won't generalize to other circumstances where the principles of medicine don't properly apply. Medicine has not been generally successful in dealing with chronic illnesses, for example, and I propose that medicine's fundamental incompleteness is the reason why it's failed. Contrary to what most people now believe, medicine is not the only healing principle, but one of a pair. And until we begin dealing with the pair, we will never be completely healed.

In order to unite the pair, we must first draw them clearly apart. Medicine and contextual healing are virtual opposites, yet they are also partners in a common quest. They are *complementary* principles—united by their differences, not by their similarities. I therefore compare them point by point—almost in polar terms—in order to make their complementary relationship clear.

In that comparing, however, I deliberately cite contextual healing's strengths and medicine's limitations—not because medicine has no strengths or contextual healing no limitations, but because I must balance an existing rhetorical and philosophical bias toward medicine. *Con-*

textual healing is the principle we're missing. Its strengths are what we need to understand. Medicine is the principle we've got. It doesn't need its obvious and well-promoted strengths listed once again; it needs a philosophic partner. I expose medicine's less obvious limitations in order to make the need for that partner clear.

By adopting this approach, I necessarily describe medicine's limitations in terms of the people who practice and sustain it—namely medical doctors and classical scientists. However, I invent for that purpose philosophic stereotypes who represent the most rigid and unbending tenets of the classical position. Some practicing physicians and scientists approach that classical stereotype. Most depart from it to greater and lesser degrees. I do not intend by my comments to portray or characterize the many dedicated and openminded physicians and scientists (among them my own personal physician) whose only motivations are to heal and to seek the truth. I believe most of them will accept the sort of partnership between the principles that I am proposing.

I have written this book because our healthcare system seems to have lost its bearings. An article in the *Journal of the American Medical Association* calls the system "out of control . . . an enormous national problem."[2] Could any portion of that problem, I am asking, be due to the fact that Nature has blessed us with *two* healing principles while we have accepted only one?

I develop that possibility by presenting critical issues that divide us. Perhaps, in the minds of some, my frankness will seem to affirm the dividing, or even deepen it. I have faith, on the other hand, that others will share with me the task of honestly examining the issues I present here. And then, by seeing the issues clearly, and by sensing what it has cost us to allow them to divide us, perhaps we will find grounds for becoming whole again.

1

Old Ideas, New Life

For all the good they do, our healing professions are themselves not well. They are beset by bickering and territorial disputes. They spend billions of dollars on research, yet consistently promise more than they deliver. Their costs escalate nearly out of control, yet the therapies we pay for sometimes do us more harm than good. Roughly nine of ten Americans say they're dissatisfied with our health-care system and would like to see it change.[1]

In part, at least, the illness within our healing professions is philosophical—a case of believing things that aren't true. For example, those who seek to heal often believe that a single healing principle or method will do, or that one healing principle, in some *absolute* sense, is better than all the rest. Not all who would be healers suffer this malady, but enough of them do to make it an important national concern.

Medical doctors, for example, deal almost exclusively with the properties and effects of molecules. They define illnesses in molecular terms, and generally apply molecular cures—drugs, most often, or, more recently, the direct manipulation of genes. And they tend to believe their molecular approach is the only healing principle, not simply one of a set.

Chiropractors, in contrast, deal almost exclusively with the spine. They identify spinal "subluxations"—maladjustments—which they then correct by adjusting the spine with their hands. Federal judge Susan Getzendanner found the American Medical Association guilty of a criminal conspiracy to destroy the profession of chiropractic through a variety of antichiropractic attacks.[2] Yet if chiropractors combat such attacks by laying claim to some absolute superiority of their own, they suffer the malady as well.

The same point applies to homeopaths, herbalists, acupuncturists, massage therapists, nutritional counselors, or anyone else in the healing arts. *There is no single healing principle*, and for anyone who believes there is, I recommend, as therapy, the following:

> Place a drop of water in the focus of your mind's eye. See it falling—bulbous, transparent, glistening, vibrating—gentle as summer rain.
>
> Now see the drop in the context of a wintry storm. Winds assault it, yet it does not entirely disperse, for a part of it freezes, diamondlike, around a tiny nucleus, which grows outward, gathering other water molecules onto its spreading tips, until at last the raindrop (or its equivalent) unfolds into the perfect hexagonal crystals of a snowflake.[3]

What *single* principle creates a snowflake? May we credit the water molecules alone? They obviously play a role, since they give snowflakes their six-sided symmetry? Yet identical molecules exist in raindrops, and raindrops don't have six-sided symmetry, so molecules alone can't call snowflakes into being.

Temperature also operates here. Raindrops don't have six-sided symmetry because they're not cold enough to show it. To create snowflakes from raindrops, therefore, we've got to turn down the temperature and freeze the molecules in place.

Yet simple freezing also creates hail, which can be as lumpy and unsymmetrical as coal. Snowflakes require yet another factor—a particular swirling of wind—which disperses the water into the unique, lacy fineness of separate and individual flakes.

All of these factors—molecules, temperature, and wind—operate at the same time. No single one of them can claim to be the key.

Our bodies are like snowflakes in this regard. Just as many things affect a snowflake, so also do many things affect us. And when the effect we seek is to be healed, no single one of those things can claim to be the key.

Adjusting the Context of Our Cells

The many things that affect us form our *context*, which essentially means "all that surrounds us." We *interact* with our context, and so its nature affects our nature. When our context changes, we change, and the instant we stop interacting with our context, we die.

To fully appreciate the power of our context, and to see how it relates to our health, we must see that it is *adjustable*. Imagine, for example, an apparatus for creating snowflakes—a chamber of some sort, perhaps, with three levers on the front. The first lever adjusts an inlet valve for spraying water into the chamber, the second adjusts temperature, and the third adjusts a current of wind.

The contours of the chamber have also been specially shaped to set the wind swirling in a particular course. Vents and drains let the air and water flow out.

First we nudge up the water lever; the chamber fills with a fine spray. Next we nudge down the temperature lever and the spray begins to freeze. Finally we adjust the wind lever and end up with slush, not snow. Some setting must be wrong.

So we play with the levers again, tinkering with the spray, fiddling with the temperature, fine-tuning the wind, until at last the flakes begin to form. We have called forth a snowstorm from cold, wind, and rain, yet no one of them alone can claim a snowflake as its own.

This principle operating here is this. When the context of a natural system changes, *it* changes—often in totally surprising ways. We simply cannot know how a natural system will *express* itself by looking at its *inner* nature alone.

For example, if we disregard the differences that come from context, raindrops and snowflakes are really the same. Both consist of ordinary H_2O molecules. To change from one *expression* of H_2O (raindrops) to another *expression* of H_2O (snowflakes), we don't do a thing to the molecules. We change their context, and the molecules spontaneously change how they behave.

Our body operates by this same principle. Eye cells and skin cells are different expressions of the same molecular system—the genes our parents gave us. The potential within that single set of genes is almost endless, and to produce a particular expression of it—a particular size, shape, or behavior in a cell—we don't have to alter the genes, just the context that sustains them.

We came into existence by this principle. We began as a single cell formed by the union of egg and sperm. Nine months later, we were delivered—a bustling bundle of trillions of cells, all of them different, all of them descended from that first solitary cell, and all of them—despite their apparent differences—governed by the self-same set of genes. Genes create the possibilities; *context* calls forth the facts.

In principle, we could build a cell-transforming device along the lines of our a water-transforming device, except the levers would be many more than two or three. They would have the same general function, however—adjusting the context inside a chamber—and if we placed a fertilized cell within the chamber, we could (in principle) manipulate the various levers and transform the cell through a variety of different states. We would be dealing again with a single molecular system—the genes—but given the complexity of both the system and its context, the possible *expressions* of that single molecular system would be almost endless.[4]

Special chambers actually *do* exist for transforming systems of genes into various kinds of cells. We call such chambers "wombs," and their entire purpose is to provide a context for developing embryonic cells. Wombs don't have levers, but mothers have other means of adjusting the context they provide. Diet choices are context adjustments for both the mother and her child. So is the decision to smoke or not to smoke. A mother's thoughts become a context for her developing child, and so does her relationship with her spouse. By adjusting her own context, a mother adjusts her child's context. And within the boundaries of the possibilities set by that single system of genes, the context she creates for herself determines the state of her child's health.

To repeat, the principle operating here is this: The same *molecular* system (whether a drop of water or a living cell) can express itself in many different ways. The differences are called forth and sustained by the *context* of the system.

By this principle, every element of our context becomes a potential healer—a potential *adjuster* of the state
of our cells. Cancer is a state of our cells. Is there a
context adjustment—or more likely, a *set* of context
adjustments—that will heal it? Arthritis is a state of our
cells. Do particular context adjustments create it? Can
other particular context adjustments cause it to go away?
We may repeat the question for diabetes, heart disease,
Alzheimer's, chronic fatigue, PMS, obesity, allergies,
and a host other chronic degenerative states. Are all of
them—or even some of them—context-dependent expressions of our single system of genes? And if so, can
context adjustments of an opposite sort transform them
back into health?

Discovering Contextual Science

Let's assume for a moment that the answer is *Yes*—that
by adjusting our natural context we can both cause
chronic illnesses and heal them. I want to emphasize,
however, that actually *committing* to such an assumption is
hardly a glib, inconsequential step, for it places us in the
uncomfortable position of being *unscientific*—at least
from the classical point of view.

Classical science is reductionistic. That means it at-
tempts to reduce systems down to their tiny parts. The
body's tiny parts are molecules. Classically speaking,
therefore, we are scientific if we study the body's molecules
(genes, enzymes, hormones, and so on), but we are
*un*scientific if we assume that context variables (diet,
thoughts, relationships, and so on) affect how those
molecules work. Classical science (the foundation of
modern medicine) doesn't even incorporate context
variables into its point of view. This is why nonmedical
healers who commit to the context perspective typically

find themselves routinely and soundly condemned—by orthodox, classical scientists, at least.

Fortunately, however, these context ideas aren't as unscientific as they used to be because science is no longer wholly reductionistic. Broad segments of science have abandoned the classical point of view precisely because it doesn't deal with context. For example, Ilya Prigogine, who won a 1977 Nobel Prize for developing a nonreductionistic, context-oriented point of view in chemistry, says that classical science suffers from an "inability to include in its theoretical frame vast areas of the relationship between man and his environment."[5] What Prigogine calls "environment" I'm calling "context." By defining how we relate to our context, Prigogine has expanded science, and allowed it to cover new aspects of our nature that classical science has consistently ignored.

Prigogine isn't the only prominent scientist to abandon the classical point of view. In recent years, this context-oriented perspective has become a scientific "growth industry." At one time or another, I've heard it called chaos theory, bifurcation theory, the theory of dissipative structures (Prigogine's term), nonequilibrium thermodynamics, nonlinear thermodynamics, synergetics, and the science of complex systems—imposing phrases all.

Of those possible names, "the science of complex systems" is the easiest to understand, but it's also a bit off target, as Gregoire Nicolis and Ilya Prigogine point out in their recent book *Exploring Complexity*. They introduce the snowflake example and then say:

> This example teaches us an important lesson: It is more natural, or at least less ambiguous, to speak of *complex behavior* than complex systems.[6]

Water molecules are not themselves complex, they're saying, but under certain circumstances they *behave* complexly, and that *complex behavior*—not the details of the system itself—is what we're interested in. Since variations in that complex behavior depend on *contextual* changes, I'll be referring to *contextual science* from now on. I mean by that term, however, the general scientific approach that is most commonly called "chaos theory."

"Parameters" of Health

Nicolis and Prigogine describe the most important discovery of this new "contextual science" in these words:

> We see that the same system can appear in different aspects.[7]

This is the point I've been making almost from the beginning. Raindrops and snowflakes are different aspects—different *expressions*—of a system of water molecules. Eye cells and skin cells are different *expressions* of a system of DNA molecules. In fact, an entire human body is just another expression of that same system of DNA molecules, and when a body gets chronically sick, it may simply have shifted from an expression that's harmonious and strong to another expression that's not.

In that case, we may define our healing task as somehow getting the system to *shift back*, and Nicolis and Prigogine tell us how we might do it:

> We want to express the idea that evolution [from one complex behavior to another] is influenced by variation of some *parameters* present in the problem that can be modified by the external world.[8]

Those "parameters" are like the levers on our hypothetical context-adjusting devices. For a snowflake, the parameters are things like temperature, wind velocity, and the amount of water in the air. By the same principle, the body has its own adjustable parameters. I'm suggesting that they are simple and natural things—the kind of food we eat, whether or not we exercise, and the kind of thoughts we think. As Nicolis and Prigogine point out, these parameters can be "modified by the external world"—that is, by us. Since they represent dimensions of our context, we'll call them "context parameters," and consider them our "levers": they are whatever we have to adjust in order to transform the body through all of its natural expressions.

Universal Principles

It may seem strange generalizing from snowflakes to bodies. Yet contextual scientists, who study complex behavior in a wide variety of natural systems, are quick to point out that their approach allows this generalizing. Unlike classical science (which tends to generate lots of narrow specialties), contextual science addresses common principles that apply to systems of any sort—electrical, chemical, physical, social, or whatever. As Mitchell Feigenbaum—one of the founders of contextual science—put it, "the theory of this behavior is *universal.*"[9]

Another of the founders, Hermann Haken, is emphatic on this point. He asks, in essence, "Could it really be true that the same general principles govern behaviors in both living and nonliving things?"

> This might have seemed absurd to many scientists. Why should systems consisting of components as different as electrons, atoms, molecules,

photons, cells, animals, or even humans be
governed by the same principles . . . ? But the past
decade has brought an abundance of evidence
indicating that this is, indeed, the case.[10]

This "universality" is why we can look at snowflakes
and learn about bodies. Contextually speaking, the same
general principles govern them both. And the message
of those governing principles is this: the human body can
express itself in a variety of states. And we may transform
it from state to state by adjusting its "context parameters"—
the various dimensions of the context that sustains it.

Inflow, Outflow, Structure, Mind

So what are the body's context parameters? For one
thing, they are substances that flow into us. Our present
substantial bulk didn't exist in that first fertilized cell any
more than the bulk of an apple tree exists in its seed. As
physicist David Bohm points out, a seed is little more
than a bundle of molecular information: "The seed has
information, in the form of DNA, which is transmitted to
the matter out of which a plant is eventually formed."[11] Our
"human seed"—that single cell from which we develop—
also contains information in the form of DNA, and the
DNA transmits its organizing information to the matter
out of which we are formed. Obviously, that matter, or
substance, must flow into us from our context, with our
main source of substance being food.

We also receive energy from our context. This energy
acts as a "driving force." Without energy drawn from
our context, the activity of our genes would run down
and die. They are "driven"—*we* are "driven"—by energy
that flows into us, and energy, like substance, may be of
various sorts.

It includes, for example, our sensory experiences. Are we therefore affected by the colors we surround ourselves with, the music we listen to, the books we read, the movies we see, the degree of clutter or order we display in our homes? These sensory parameters are adjustable, to be sure. Is it too far a stretch to believe they also affect our health?

And what about the electromagnetic radiation we experience from high-voltage power lines, for another example, or from the monitors on our home computers? Is electromagnetic radiation an adjustable parameter that affects us?

Taken together, these and other sources of substance and energy make up a general category of context parameters that we might call *inflow*.

Our relationship with our context depends on more than what flows into us, however. It also includes our *outflow*, or what flows back into our context from us. We *interact* with our context, and our context parameters cover both sides of that interaction—what we receive and what we give back—our inflow *and* our outflow, in other words.

Exercise and elimination are obvious outflow parameters, but what about the things we say and do? Does their quality affect our health? Does it matter that we yell at our children or act in selfish ways? Lie detectors pick up physiological evidence of our fibs. Is truthfulness therefore an outflow parameter? Can being honest help make us healthy and strong?

Context may also include *structural constraints*. Laser devices depend, for example, on "a particular cavity structure."[12] That means the light has to bounce back and forth within a cavity, or a chamber, that's been very precisely shaped. Perhaps we also have particular "cavity structures" or other precisely formed shapes that sustain us.

Hermann Haken personally feels "that the laser can serve as a paradigm of action of neuronal [nerve] networks."[13] If Haken's feeling is even close to true, our nerves probably need "a particular cavity structure" as well, which may be one function of the spine. Chiropractors say the spine can get "subluxated," meaning that the cavity it provides can get out of adjustment. If the cavity of a laser device got "subluxated," would the laser device still work? Probably not. Perhaps it's not unreasonable to believe, therefore, that a subluxated spine might affect the operation of our nerves. Or that a chiropractor's adjustments might set them right. The various massage techniques may be affecting structural parameters as well.

I suggest, finally, that the *mind* is one of our context parameters. Scientifically, the mind is hard to pin down, but that doesn't mean it's not real. Even René Descartes, one of the founders of classical science, acknowledged the mind, although he drew mind and body irrevocably apart. Contextual healing puts them back together again by assuming that the body is the *instrument* of the mind. From that perspective, some sort of coupling must exist—a coupling that places the body subject to the mind rather than (or at least in addition to) the reverse.

Our mind receives *information* from our context. In purely physical terms, that information has a certain absolute existence, but that's not what we experience. We experience our *interpretations*, which are not absolute, but variable. These variable interpretations establish what we call our "states of mind," and to the degree that we may *adjust* our states of mind they become one of our context parameters—a "lever" we may set to influence the state of our health.

Inflow, outflow, structure, and mind—parameters of context, adjusters of health. Healers have been talking about these sorts of things for over two thousand years, but there's been no science to explain them. We've had a rich history of practical experiences, but no framework for making sense of them, and in our sophisticated culture (which expects things to make something more than *common* sense), that's been a scientific kiss of death.

I propose a resurrection. "New Explanation Breathes Life into Old Ideas," the headline announcing it might read. The new explanation is the contextual science of Ilya Prigogine's 1977 Nobel Prize. The old ideas are the same as they've always been, but they can be summarized now within a certain unifying theme. That theme is the principle we've been echoing: The human body is more than the molecules that make it up. It depends absolutely on its context, and context changes can transform it. Contextual healing links *context changes* to states of health.

A Profound Difference in Scale

Now, how does contextual healing differ from conventional medicine? First of all, medicine follows the tradition of classical science. It deals, in other words, with molecules, which are the system's tiny parts. Medical scientists study DNA, hormones, enzymes, neurotransmitters, and so on—which is to say that they study the molecular details of the system itself. They do not study—nor, as a rule, do they concern themselves with—contextual matters of the sort we've been talking about. Medicine tends not to accept the idea that a system can "misbehave" without its molecular mechanisms being broken down, so it concerns itself—in molecular terms—with *system repair,* or *system control.*

Contextual healers care little for the tiny details of the system because they consider the system fixed, or given—a constant, in other words, not a variable. They operate from the premise that the same system, despite its fundamentally constant nature, can *behave* in different ways, depending on the context, so if the system happens to "misbehave," they generally count it a context problem—a matter of adjusting *external* parameters—and don't seek to repair or control the system itself.

The two healing disciplines operate, therefore, on completely different scales. Medicine is microscopic. Doctors can't see their tiny molecular subject matter with their ordinary senses, so they use instruments and devices to see what they think they need to see. And since their subject matter is so far below the scale of normal life, they tend to talk about things we ordinary patients can't understand.

Contextual healing, on the other hand, is macroscopic. Its scale is the scale of daily life, so it tends to have a normal, everyday feeling about it. Contextual healers can view their subject matter through their ordinary senses, so they hardly ever use instruments, and they generally talk about things we can understand.

Hermann Haken expresses the macroscopic focus of contextual science in these words:

> The order parameters [context parameters] are the macroscopic observables, which describe the macroscopic behavior of the system. . . . Once the macroscopic observables are given the behavior of the microscopic elements is determined.[14]

In other words, once we set the context parameters, the details of the system take care of themselves. As a consequence, we can govern the details of the system by changing its context parameters, which are macroscopic in scale. But we *cannot* govern the system's macroscopic behavior by working with the microscopic details alone.

A Matter of Different Goals

Medicine and contextual healing also have different goals. Drugs are like detailed commands to the body. They contain information pertaining to specific chemical reactions, so they tell the body exactly what to do. Insulin, for example, amounts to a command to transport sugar across cell membranes and into our cells.

Context parameters don't contain that kind of specific information. They have nothing to do with the details of the body's molecular behavior. They sustain that behavior, but they don't direct it. Here's how a contextual scientist expresses this thought: "The [context] parameter . . . has a very modest information content, and can not prescribe the new state of the system. This new state then arises mainly as an *independent* response of the system to an environmental change."[15]

In a snowflake, for example, wind contains no information about six-sidedness, yet a snowflake can't assume a six-sided shape without the wind. For a snowflake, wind isn't a command; it's an opportunity.

Imagine planting two seeds side by side. You nurture both seeds with the same nutrients, but one ends up a petunia, the other ends up a rose. Nutrients don't tell a seed what to do, but they do sustain it.

The information that tells a plant what to do resides in its genes. But unless the genes receive substance and energy from the plant's context, the information they contain is useless. And since the fundamental genetic information never changes, all variations in a plant's behavior come from variations in its context, even though nothing in the context *tells* the plant what to do. Something that's absolutely *uninformative* in a detailed sense nonetheless ends up governing the plant's overall behavior. It's a bit paradoxical, but that's how it is.

And that's how it is with us, too. Our genes contain the information that guides our molecular processes. And when medical doctors give us drugs, they give us molecular commands that literally *replace*, or override, the information contained in our genes. Contextual healing, in contrast, seeks only to *empower* the genes by giving them a sustaining context. And context adjustments affect us because, since our genetic information is essentially constant, all variations in our behavior necessarily come from our context, even though nothing in our context *tells* us what to do.

Genes are our *constant* source of molecular information; context is our *variable* source of substance, energy, structure and so on. Medicine seeks to alter the constant. Contextual healing seeks to adjust the variable.

Ilya Prigogine expresses a thought that has long been contextual healing's underlying theme: "The purpose of all change, if it is in keeping with the nature of things, is to realize in each being the perfection of its intelligible essence."[16] That "intelligible essence" resides physically within the genes. Contextual healing seeks only to call it forth.

A Health-Care Smorgasbord

Medicine and contextual healing are two extremes of a scientific and practical zoom lens. Medicine is the close-up view. It penetrates our physical boundaries and explores the tiniest corners of our individual cells. It probes us with delicate instruments that transcend by many powers our ordinary feeble senses. Medicine studies the genes and their products—hormones, enzymes, and so on—in order to discern where they may have gone astray, with the goal, then, of correcting them—of intervening *at their level* and redirecting them aright. Medicine studies the molecular system itself and considers the context that empowers it a given, a constant, something of no practical concern.

Contextual healing is the wide-angle view. It seeks to serve the system's vital needs—the substances it relies on, the structures that constrain it, and the many dimensions of energy that empower it. It also proposes a role for the mind, defining the body as the instrument of the mind. It sees the molecular system of the body as the physical source of healing intelligence, and honors it, therefore, by leaving it entirely alone. Being macroscopic, contextual healing guides itself by the data of ordinary experience. And being as broad and diverse as life itself, it seeks simplicity in pattern and regularity, not in logic and rationality.

From this perspective, there is no *single* healing principle. Broadly speaking, there are at least two, and within the broad umbrella of contextual healing we may define many narrower principles as well. Some of these principles are long-term, and some more immediate in their effects. Some are gentle, and some more aggressive and intense. They operate at different levels and anchor themselves within different scientific (or even nonscientific) domains. Yet none is inherently superior (because they all have different strengths), and none may claim the world of healing as its own.

I envision, therefore, a sort of health-care smorgasbord—a wide array of healing options from which we consumers may pick and choose. I envision a diverse and dedicated corps of healers—medical doctors, chiropractors, herbalists, massage therapists, color therapists, play therapists, emotional therapists, homeopaths, and so on—working together in harmony and peace, their minds and hearts focused on the people they serve, with each healer pursuing the healing principle that best expresses his individual gift, and all directed toward the simple goal of creating and maintaining the highest expression of health. I envision a health-care system that, for all but crisis care, considers healing to be the *patient's* job, with all who would be healers assuming but a servant's role. My vision, however, is far from being real. We have no health-care smorgasbord. We have dedicated healers, but few who aren't medical doctors. There's not much peace and harmony within our healing arts, and many who would be healers aren't even allowed by law to practice their particular gift. We have a health-care system that, for the most part, considers patients incompetent, with government agencies assigned, it seems, to protect us from having to choose. And we are not getting the results we seek.

In that sense, the system that would heal us is itself not well. Does it have its own context parameters—its own parameters of *inflow* (of new ideas into the system, for example), *outflow* (the way physicians treat us, for example), *structure* (the constraints of our health-care laws, for example), and *mind* (perhaps the way we consumers think about our health) that are creating this particular state? Can we adjust those parameters to heal our health-care system as we seek to heal ourselves?

If so, we've got a whole new way of thinking to learn. Perhaps it's time to begin.

2

Casualties in a Philosophic War

From the earliest of times, contextual healers have considered illness a general state of *imbalance*. As a consequence, they tend to reject the medical concept of "disease."

To understand the difference between "disease" and "imbalance," consider a case in which medical doctors examined sixty-five patients who'd complained of stomach pain. They used standard medical diagnostic techniques, including an endoscope (a fiber-optic device that actually let them look inside each patient's stomach), and determined that the patients had peptic ulcers. All sixty-five cases had the same "disease."

The doctors didn't treat the patients, however. They took them, as an experiment, to a traditional Chinese healer, who diagnosed the patients with his own non-scientific methods, then treated them over a number of visits while the medical doctors watched.

To diagnose the patients, the Chinese healer examined their complexion, listened to the quality of their voice, and asked them what tastes they liked and didn't like. He even smelled them. And finally, after a rather lengthy series of similar probings, he carefully and intently examined each patient's pulse. He was, as one authority put it, "looking at the patient the way a painter looks at a landscape—as a particular arrangement of signs in which the essence of the whole can be seen."[1]

The Chinese healer saw within the sixty-five patients six different "patterns of disharmony." As you can see, the expression "patterns of disharmony" suggests that some harmonious pattern exists as a standard from which these patients had departed. That standard represents the state of balance, or health, against which the many possible imbalances are measured.[2]

Notice the difference in perspective. To the medical doctors, the sixty-five patients all had the same disease—peptic ulcer—as diagnosed by a battery of tests and a close-up examination through the endoscope. To the Chinese healer, the patients represented six different *patterns of imbalance*, each expressed as combinations and arrangements of such signs as a flushed face, an absence of sweating, a voice tending toward breathiness, or a thin, thready pulse. The Chinese healer didn't know, and probably wouldn't have cared, that the ulcer even existed.

The Chinese healer treated the patients for two months. His goal was to *adjust* the patterns he'd seen toward the state of balance, or health. At the end of that period, the Western physicians re-examined the patients. Fifty-three of them had recovered completely. Seven more showed significant improvement. That's an overall success rate of 92 percent.[3]

The Chinese physician would describe balance as a relationship between *yin* and *yang*. The Chinese use the terms *yin* and *yang* to represent paired opposites, which may be of any sort: hot/cold, light/dark, up/down, male/female, and so on. In general, however, the *yang* principle is active and dynamic, while the *yin* principle is calm and stabilizing. The balance, then, is between activity and calmness—between dynamism and stability.

In one form or another, this balancing of energetic extremes appears in almost every contextual system. D. D. Palmer, for example, the founder of chiropractic, believed that spinal subluxations affect health by causing body functions to become too active or two calm,[4] which the Chinese would call too *yang* or too *yin*.

Many other disorders—physical and nonphysical—fall into this same too-active-versus-too-calm arrangement:

AREA OF DISORDER	TOO ACTIVE	TOO CALM[5]
Immunity	Allergies	Infections
Blood Pressure	Hypertension	Hypotension
Emotions	Anxiety	Depression
Eating	Bulimia	Anorexia
Working	Workaholism	Laziness
Parenting	Overcontrolling	Undercontrolling
Heart Disease	Cardiac arrest	Congestive heart failure

As diverse as those conditions may seem, they express a common theme: the system isn't healthy because it isn't balanced. The healer's task, then, is to adjust the sustaining context until balance is restored, while leaving the internal system—the source of healing intelligence—free to act for itself.

Hippocrates and Contextual Healing

In this sense, Hippocrates was a contextual healer. He saw in nature some kind of self-organizing power, which he called the *physis*. Its effect, he believed, was to move us spontaneously toward a balanced state of harmony and health:

> Everything in nature tends to re-establish that perfect harmony that constitutes normal life. Every force in the individual tends to preserve a perfect equilibrium, and, if it has been disturbed, to re-establish order and harmony.[6]

Physis, of course, comes from ancient Greek. Its root is *phyo,* which means "to beget." Our English word "nature" carries in its root the same kind of thought. It comes from the Latin *nasci,* from which those who speak Spanish get *nacer—*"to be born."[7] Both *physis* and "nature" imply by their roots some sort of spontaneous unfolding—an expressing of some inherent inner wisdom.

Physis is also the root of the word "physician." As guardian of the *physis,* the physician had a clearly supporting role:

> Not a ruler or violator of nature . . . he stands ready to *aid* the healing power that is inherent.[8]

The means of aiding the *physis* were largely contextual—a matter of sustaining and empowering the body's innate intelligence, which resides physically in the genes.

The Body As a Machine

How the contextual healer Hippocrates ever became the father of modern medicine is a matter of conjecture, because, if he was medicine's father, he bore a very rebellious child:

> Through the Middle Ages and the Renaissance,
> and until the beginning of the nineteenth cen-
> tury, Hippocrates' name stood as the symbol of
> a medical wisdom that understands the nature
> of the human body as dependent on the nature
> of the universe. . . . In the course of the nineteenth
> century, [however], Hippocrates was *dethroned* as
> the scientific authority.[9]

Medicine's nineteenth-century fathers dethroned Hippocrates by rejecting his healing philosophy. They called
it (contemptuously) "vitalism," and considered it irrational and wrong. They found particularly offensive his
belief in the *physis*—the idea that the body possesses
some wellspring of inner wisdom from which healing
spontaneously unfolds.

They adopted instead the philosophy of "atomism,"
which came from another Greek philosopher named
Democritus:[10]

> Atomism may be defined as the doctrine that
> material reality is composed of simple and un-
> changeable minute particles, called atoms. It
> holds that all observable changes must be re-
> duced to changes in the configuration of these
> particles.[11]

From the atomist point of view, illness and health are
simply different configurations of atoms. Nature doesn't
prefer one over the other; they simply exist. The atoms
that compose these configurations are impartial and
indifferent—basically interchangeable, mechanical parts.
They possess no means—no independent intelligence—for
somehow rearranging themselves into some "preferred
state" called health.

If we become sick, therefore, whatever rearranging needs to be done must be imposed from the outside. This is the role atomistic physicians assume. They approach the body as "a complex piece of machinery," which, when it breaks down, "needs a mechanic and mechanical remedies to fix it."[12]

This atomism—or "mechanism," as it's sometimes called—became "an inspiring idea for the spiritual fathers of modern science."[13] It has particularly inspired molecular biology, which undergirds modern medicine. For example, Robert A. Weinberg, a prominent MIT molecular biologist and cancer specialist, recently wrote this:

> Many biologists of the future will think of a biological system in terms of a series of well-defined mechanical parts that can be dismantled, engineered, and reassembled under the guidance of the molecular mechanic.[14]

Molecular biologists, Weinberg believes, will someday invent new forms of life:

> The newly gained ability to describe and manipulate molecules . . . has made it possible to change critical elements of the biological blueprint at will, and in so doing create versions of life that were never anticipated by natural evolution. . . . The molecular biologist will no longer confront living forms as the finished products of evolution, but will be an active participant in initiating organismic change.[15]

As you can see, there's no hint here of evoking some *inherent* expression of life. On the contrary, physicians use their knowledge of nature to detect her weaknesses and flaws, which they then repair through molecular means. They create *improved* versions of life, which their knowledge has allowed them to see. Their goal is entirely hopeful—overcoming illness and death. But they achieve it without nature's help, by imposing their will from the outside.

Perhaps no one has expressed this spirit of hopeful imposing more clearly than Benjamin Rush, one of medicine's eighteenth-century founders and a signer of the Declaration of Independence. He said:

> Although physicians are in speculation the servants, yet in practice they are the masters of nature. . . . Instead of waiting for the slow operations of nature, to eliminate a supposed morbid matter from the body, art should take the business out of her hands.[16]

"The business," of course, is healing.

Newton and the Atomists' Dream

The scientist who first made mastering nature seem possible was Isaac Newton. He proposed laws of motion and the existence of gravity, a mathematically precise attractive force that governs the behavior of celestial bodies. He invented calculus to express the mathematics of his laws, and in two hours, calculated data on the trajectories of stars and planets that had taken Johannes Kepler and Tycho Brahe sixty years to produce through observation alone.[17] Furthermore, his method worked every time he applied it.

The picture Newton revealed was precisely what the atomists envisioned. It showed simple particles (large ones, in this case) governed by simple forces (gravity) as described by simple laws (the laws of gravity and motion). Based on his discoveries, Newton found himself essentially omniscient as far as the solar system was concerned. He had found a way to reveal the past and the future from data taken from the present.

To understand how successfully he did this, look at this recent example. Scientists found the following statement in an ancient Chinese document: "During the first month of the reign of King Yi, in the first month of spring, the sun rose twice at Zheng." The phrase that caught their eye was "the sun rose twice at Zheng." They assumed that the double-rising referred to a solar eclipse, and when they applied Newton's laws, they discovered that an eclipse of the sun actually *did* occur at that exact location on the morning of April 21, 889 B.C.[18] By reversing the process, they could just as easily have predicted whatever eclipses might occur at Zheng in the future.

Newton seemed to prove that the present, given the past, can be only what it is. And the future, given the present, can unfold only as it must. Future events are *determined* by the present as present events are *determined* by the past. The present not only connects the past and the future, it also "contains" them, or at least evidence of what they must inevitably be. Newton showed astronomers how to reveal the past and the future of planetary systems by putting present data into calculus formulas and running those formulas backward or forward through time. And he inspired faith that other scientists, in other areas of science, might do the very same thing.

Science's Messiah

For many early scientists, Newton's discoveries fulfilled scripture. God had given Man "dominion" over all the earth,[19] and scientists, under Newton's inspired hand, now expected to claim it. Newton's laws were the laws of God Himself.

One nineteenth-century scientist praised Newton in these worshipful words:

> Announcing the coming of science's Messiah...
> Whom Plato revered, and He was called Newton.
> He came, he revealed the principle supreme,
> Eternal, universal, One and unique as God Himself.
> The worlds were hushed, he spoke: ATTRACTION.
> This word was the very word of creation.[20]

Newton's triumph seemed to confirm the principle of "determinism"—the idea that nature, at some fundamental level, is simple, logical, predictable, and inevitable. Today, determinism and science are virtual synonyms, as Alfred North Whitehead points out:

> I mean the inexpugnable belief that every detailed occurrence can be correlated with its antecedents in a perfectly definite manner, exemplifying general principles. Without this belief the incredible labours of scientists would be without hope.[21]

The rise of determinism spelled the end of vitalism. No longer was it scientifically acceptable to believe in an inner intelligence that expressed itself as a healing power. Emil Du Bois-Reymond, a nineteenth-century German physiologist, pointed out this direct contradiction between science and vitalism:

> A deficiency in the conception of vitalism is first of all very much on the surface. We have seen

that all motion . . . [is] divisible into straightlined movements and forces between the presumed particles of matter. This has not been taken into consideration at all with that idea.[22]

The idea that "all motion . . . [is] divisible into straightlined movements and forces between presumed particles of matter" comes straight from Isaac Newton.

Discovering Cause and Effect

It seemed now that everything in nature must consist of tiny particles lawfully connected by gravitylike forces of attraction. Biological scientists fully expected, therefore, to be as successful in their domain as Newton was in his. They began by seeking to understand the body according to the explanations of their day.[23] Some scientists suggested that chemicals in the body exploded like gunpowder.[24] Others envisioned a bubbly sort of energy like fermentation.[25] To explain how such forces might move muscles, they proposed systems of shunts and valves, imagining us to be very much like their machines.[26]

And they tried to test their explanations. An Italian scientist named Borelli concluded that explosions and fermentations, being gaseous sorts of forces, must show themselves under water as bubbles. So he held an animal under water, and as it struggled to survive, he slit its muscles with a knife. When he saw no bubbles along the slit, he concluded that the forces weren't explosions or fermentations after all.[27] So scientists struggled on to find other deterministic principles to account for the existence of life.

A breakthrough came in 1786 when Luigi Galvani discovered "animal electricity."[28] Galvani touched a nerve in a severed frog's leg with a pair of scissors during an electrical storm and the leg jumped. Later, he saw a frog leg jump again when he touched it with a scalpel while an electrical machine was activated. He became convinced that the force that moves the body is electrical.

At first this seemed a turn back to vitalism. Galvani even called his animal electricity "a heretofore neglected innate, vital force."[29] Other people hoped to equate electricity and Life itself.[30]

But scientists soon explained the body's electricity in purely chemical terms, and they explained chemistry in terms of gravitylike forces of attraction of the sort Newton proposed. In principle, these explanations and discoveries made the body as predictable as the heavens and entirely governed (like a frog's leg) by *cause* (Galvani touched the frog's leg) and *effect* (the frog's leg jumped). All need for an *inner* intelligence seemed to have disappeared.

A Move to Oust Vitalism

A move to oust vitalism now began in earnest. Elie Cyon (a Russian physiologist) spoke of his "determination to evict vitalism from physiology."[31] Emil Du Bois-Reymond, the German physiologist I mentioned a moment ago, held this same goal with a colleague named Ernst Wilhelm von Brucke: "Brucke and I, we have both sworn to expose the truth, namely that there are no other forces operating in the organism except those physico-chemical ones."[32]

The assault against vitalism succeeded. The final holdout against the assault was Eduoard Pfluger, who died in 1910—"the last eminent physiologist to retain a trace of vitalism."[33] Pfluger's death represented "the release of natural science from [vitalism's] bonds."[34] Science had now became wholly and completely atomistic.

An Orthodox Point of View

Atomism's victory established medicine as the scientifically orthodox point of view. All other points of view—especially those that descend from the vitalist tradition of Hippocrates—became unscientific by definition.

In contrast to the contextual notion of "imbalance," the starting point for the orthodox medical view is the idea that diseases are specific "entities,"[35] or things. We reflect this thinglike view of disease in our popular speech. We talk about "catching" a disease, or "giving" a disease to someone as if we were exchanging Christmas gifts. By this perspective, people "have" AIDS, much as they might have watches or freckles. Or consider this quote from a health columnist in the 1930s: "Surgery does the ideal thing: it separates the patient from his disease. It puts the patient back to bed and the disease in a bottle."[36]

Orthodox medicine defines diseases as entities in order to classify them, or organize them into a "taxonomy." The taxonomy of diseases then becomes the framework for defining and organizing medicine's therapies. In this sense, diseases are the subject matter of medicine, just as plants are the subject matter of botany.

Historically, a parallel between medicine and botany exists. The first taxonomy of living things was published in 1735 by the Swedish botanist Carolus Linnaeus. His taxonomy was a hierarchy of kingdoms, phyla, classes, orders, and so on. Not many years later, the Frenchman Francois Boissier de Sauvages published the first taxonomy of diseases, broken down in almost exactly the same way. He began with ten classes, divided them into forty orders, and finally ended up at the bottom with more than 2,400 "species" of diseases, each as real, in an abstract scientific sense, as tulips or black-eyed Susans.[37]

Today virtually every aspect of medicine hinges on
the modern version of this taxonomy of diseases. The
National Library of Medicine publishes a 470-page "tree
structure" of medical subjects,[38] in which section C,
which is eighty-seven pages long, covers "Diseases." Its
entries look like this:

Virus diseases
  Arbovirus Infections
    Encephalitis, Epidemic
      Encephalitis, California
      Encephalitis, Japanese B
      Encephalitis, St. Louis
      Encephalitis, Tick-borne
        Louping Ill
        etc.

Within medicine, the specialty called "nosology" establishes these classifications. In a recent case, a committee of the American Psychiatric Association assembled to
decide whether or not premenstrual syndrome (PMS)
should be recognized as an official disease. Some of the
issues were scientific, such as whether medicine knew
enough about PMS. [39] Other issues were social—how
recognizing PMS would affect insurance payments, for
example, and whether it would stigmatize women and
reinforce primitive myths about "raging hormones." In
the end, the committee voted to give PMS quasi-official
recognition by including it in an appendix of the Association's basic manual of diseases.[40]

Having defined a disease, medical scientists next try
to understand it in molecular terms. If a germ causes it,
they want to know which germ, and how it does its
destructive work. If it's caused by some molecular breakdown in the body (like the pancreas not making enough
insulin), they want to know the chemicals involved and
where the breakdown is occurring. Their goal is to

develop *rational* therapies. In principle, rational therapies protect them against making mistakes:

> Rational drug therapy avoids undesirable situations by starting only with rational ideas for new drug products, and then implementing these ideas with sound scientific research.[41]

This quest for rationality is one reason why medical research takes so long and costs so much. Even in the best of cases, researchers may take decades just understanding a disease, let alone curing it. Cancer researchers argue, for example, that "genetic discoveries have led to a better understanding of cancer," and that "progress cannot be measured by the number of cures."[42] They are still pinning down the molecular details.

Once they grasp the details of a disease, they seek to correct whatever has gone wrong to cause it. They generally do this either by *stimulating* particular chemical operations or *inhibiting* them. Not surprisingly, the two kinds of drugs involved are called (1) stimulants and (2) inhibitors.

Most of the time, these pharmaceutical stimulants and inhibitors are based on the body's own natural chemicals. In essence, such drugs give medical doctors tools for communicating with the body in its own "language"—for directing its behavior in the very manner it uses to direct itself.

Between 1910 (when the last "eminent" vitalist died) and today, this orthodox view has become a tremendous enterprise with two basic divisions: (1) medical research and (2) medical practice. In principle, medical researchers develop proven molecular therapies, which they then deliver to medical practitioners who apply them. As our legislators have become increasingly concerned about health care, they have generally accepted the medical point of view, which says that classical scientific rationality is our best protection against error and fraud. As a consequence, our health-care laws make it very difficult for anything nonmedical to be accepted as valid.

This is why we don't have a broad health-care smorgasbord of the sort I envisioned in the first chapter. Our ancestors waged a philosophic war, and medicine won. The losers were the contextual healers—the vitalists—the people who sought ways to express an inner healing power. Their contextual healing practices got condemned scientifically and sentenced, in essence, to die.

They were condemned because the principles of classical science couldn't explain them. Paradoxically, this was considered *their* weakness, not a weakness of classical science itself. Contextual healers presented the evidence of their experience, but classical scientists said their evidence simply couldn't be. This was a time when people trusted their logic more than their senses. As it turns out, that's not always a wise thing to do.

3

Blind Spots in the Classical View

The logic of classical science began to break down roughly a century ago. One of the first scientists to sense something amiss was a brilliant French mathematician named Henri Poincarè.

Poincarè was trying to discover mathematically if the universe is stable. Most scientists thought the answer was obvious. Newton had shown how entirely predictable planetary systems are, and the universe certainly *seemed* to be stable. But Newton's laws, Poincarè knew, work only when scientists ignore tiny losses of energy—like the friction that gradually slows a pendulum.

This bothered Poincarè because planets and moons experience these energy losses too. For example, the moon's gravitational tug creates the rising and falling of tides, which means that the tides also tug against the orbit of the moon. This causes a tiny frictionlike loss of energy that Newton's laws weren't taking into account.

The scientists who study these energy losses call them "dissipations," from the verb "to dissipate," which means "to vanish by dispersion."[1] In a sense, the crowd that gathers to watch a three-alarm fire dissipates—vanishes by dispersion—once the fire's been put out. A pendulum's energy dissipates through friction, and tiny amounts of the moon's energy dissipate through the simple tug of the tides. Everyone assumed that tiny dissipations must surely have tiny and inconsequential effects, but no one could really be sure.

Planets and moons also dissipate energy as a consequence of the *three-body problem*. The three-body problem comes from the fact that two orbiting bodies experience at least *some* small gravitational tug from any third body, no matter how small it is or how far away. Most scientists simply ignored this small complication—this small dissipation, or loss of the system's energy—but Poincarè harbored some doubts.

His doubts came from the fact that no one had ever solved a three-body problem before. They'd solved two-body problems, which are clean and neat because there aren't any extraneous gravitational tugs to worry about. And they'd learned to *approximately* solve three-body problems by more or less edging toward the correct answer through a series of successive approximations. But the presence of that extra dissipation, tiny though it may have been, meant that their three-body calculations were never *exactly* right, so Poincarè knew he couldn't be *absolutely* confident the universe was stable. He hoped to discover a mathematical proof that would allow him to conclude that it was.

What Poincarè discovered caused him great distress. Through a series of tedious calculations, he discovered that problems involving more than two bodies simply can't be solved. Extra bodies inevitably cause small dissipations, most of which can be guessed at or ignored. But Poincarè found cases—completely *unpredictable* cases—

where even the tiniest third-body disturbance could have explosively chaotic effects, turning orbits erratic and sending them careering off into space.

Poincarè understood that the same basic problem would affect *all* natural systems, even the simplest ones. "These things are so bizarre," he said, "that I cannot bear to contemplate them." They seemed to undermine the very foundations of science as he knew it. Classical science grew from an entirely reasonable assumption—that tiny causes necessarily have tiny effects, so we can ignore all but the most prominent ones. Poincarè had shown that the classical assumption was a myth.

No one paid attention, however, because Poincarè discovered these things shortly before two new ways of thinking completely captured classical science. Neither of the new ways of thinking—quantum mechanics and general relativity—addressed the problem Poincarè had seen, yet they distracted scientists so completely that hardly anyone paid attention to what he was trying to say. For almost a century, Poincarè's unsettling observations about the inherent *unreliability* of classical science got overrun by a blind commitment to the *absolute certainty* of scientific truth.[2]

In recent years, however, scientists like Nobel Laureate Ilya Prigogine have rediscovered and redefined Poincarè's unsettling observations, launching in the process a new approach to science—the contextual science that we've been talking about. As a consequence, classical science is losing its once preeminent place. "The Golden Age of Classical Science is gone," Prigogine writes, "and with it also the conviction that Newtonian rationality, even with its various conflicting interpretations, forms a suitable basis for our dialogue with nature."[3]

Not everyone agrees, of course. One critic charges that Prigogine and his context-oriented colleagues fall "somewhere in the spectrum bounded by responsible science and the Maharishi Mahesh Yogi's Technology of the Unified Field."[4] Another claims that they "live in the twilight zone of scientific credibility."[5] The critics, however, are confirmed classical scientists whose ideas are being replaced.

An Adjustable Variable

Classical ideas are being replaced because Poincarè's observations reveal an important truth. The energy that drives dynamic systems *dissipates*, and if it's not replenished by energy from an outside source, the systems will die. Classical science ignores this constant dissipating and replenishing of energy, yet it turns out to be a fact so basic that it even describes the behavior of an ordinary kitchen sink.

Imagine, for example, a sink filled with six inches of water. The drain is stopped up, the faucet shut off. The water is calm and settled—at *equilibrium*, we say, because equilibrium, in essence, means "stillness."

Now imagine the same sink with both the faucet and the drain wide open and going full blast. Now the water roils with turbulent energy. The amount of water in the sink may remain exactly the same, but it isn't at equilibrium anymore. It's *far from equilibrium*—far from stillness.

Or imagine the same sink, but this time with a stirring device installed—some sort of rotating blade. With the stirring device turned off, the water settles at equilibrium. But if we turn it on, the water starts to move, and as we increase the stirring device's velocity, the water moves ever more rapidly until eventually we can have it roiling with the same turbulent energy as before, only this time by a different means. Regardless of the difference in means, the system is still far from equi-librium—far from stillness—because energy is being added to it from the outside.

We may now envision what amounts to a scale, or a ruler, for measuring a very important property called *distance from equilibrium*. At the low end of the scale sits the stillness of equilibrium itself. At the high end of the scale sits the very *un*still state of maximum turbulence, which is as far from equilibrium as you can get. Between equilibrium on the one end and maximum turbulence on the other we see many possible distances from equi-librium ranging from small to great.

Distance from equilibrium represents the fact that the same molecular system may be driven by many possible levels of energy and activity that enter into it from the outside. Two terms I'll be referring to from now on—"close to equilibrium" and "far from equilibrium"—refer explicitly to positions along this scale, and they mean, in essence, "close to stillness" and "far from stillness," with the difference being based on the strength of the energy that drives the system.

Distance from equilibrium is the adjustable factor that governs the system's overall behavior. As we operate the faucet and the drain or as we change the velocity of the stirring device, the water molecules in the sink don't change, but their behavior does. We have shifted the distance from equilibrium of the system as a whole.

Let's consider another example or two. Imagine a boulder sitting at the base of a hill. It is at equilibrium because it is still. Now you begin pushing the boulder up the hill. You are pushing it away from equilibrium, or away from its position of stillness, and the higher up the hill you push it, the farther from equilibrium it goes. It *gains* energy, in fact (the energy of your effort), as you can readily see by letting it go.

Or imagine a river flowing toward the ocean. The closer the water gets to the ocean, the closer to *gravitational* equilibrium it gets. When it reaches the ocean, it could, in principle, settle into the stillness of equilibrium, but it probably won't. Instead it will most likely get lifted away from equilibrium by some other energy source—the energy of a gale, perhaps, or the brisk flowing of natural currents.

In general, distance from equilibrium represents a concept called "internal energy."[6] That's the amount of energy in the system that can be used for doing work. Still water has no internal energy. Strongly flowing water—water that is far from equilibrium—is filled with it.

Your pushing the boulder up the hill moved it away from equilibrium and gave it energy for doing work. Evaporation lifts water away from equilibrium and gives it energy for doing work, which we see in the rainfall's falling, which becomes the river's flowing, which drives the electric generators that empower the appliances in our homes. Energy that flows *into* a system lifts it away from equilibrium; energy that flows *out of* a system moves it toward equilibrium and dilutes its capacity to do work.

And this is why Poincarè's concern with those tiny dissipations proved to be so crucial. *Dissipation depletes internal energy*, and no matter how tiny it is, if it's not replaced, it will eventually run the system dry. Classical science doesn't take this simple idea into account.

Now, with this background, we are prepared to introduce what is probably the most important point in our discussion so far: *living human bodies exist far from equilibrium*. We are sustained far from equilibrium by our high degree of internal energy, which we must constantly replenish.[7] The fact that bodies maintain themselves far from equilibrium makes them fundamentally different from pendulums and springs and planetary systems, which exist *close* to equilibrium and may therefore be described by classical scientific laws.

The point of Poincarè's discovery was that classical science can't deal *reliably* with systems that dissipate energy, and that includes all systems that exist away from equilibrium. And it can't deal *at all* with systems that exist far from equilibrium. As Ilya Prigogine explains, "the deterministic view of chemistry *fails* when far-from-equilibrium processes are involved."[8] Classically speaking, "with two pendulums coupled through a spring, a single pendulum forced periodically from the outside, or three interacting masses (the celebrated three-body problem), we arrive at the frontier of present knowledge."[9] The challenges of illness and health lie well beyond that classical frontier.

Balance and the "Just Right" Principle

In one sense, these ideas are new. Yet in another sense, they're as old as nature. Practically speaking, they've always affected us. We're simply catching up—bringing into our science what's always been part of our life.

Perhaps we may therefore forgive the old-time contextual healers if they say, "We told you so." For centuries they've borne the mocking of classical scientists, yet in many striking ways their ideas parallel the principles of this new contextual science.

To see one such parallel, let's refine how we describe our hypothetical snowflake machine. We will now see it as a device for adjusting *distance from equilibrium* along three different dimensions of context. The first lever adjusts how fast the water flows into the chamber; the second lever adjusts how hot or cold the chamber gets; and the third lever adjusts how fast the wind blows through the chamber. The three levers adjust different aspects of the sustaining context, yet the *underlying variable* that they adjust is the same. That underlying variable is *distance from equilibrium*, which may vary along a range that runs from low to high, from close to equilibrium to far away.

And the goal of the adjusting is always the same. For each parameter and for each purpose (making snowflakes vs. making hail, for example), there's some setting—some distance from equilibrium—that's not too close, not too far away, but *just right*. This is the principle Goldilocks applied to the porridge she found in the three bears' kitchen. One bowl was too far from equilibrium, another was too close to equilibrium, and the third was just right. By the same principle, snowflakes come from just the right spray of water, just the right degree of cold, and just the right force of wind.

This "just right" principle comes straight from contextual science, but it sounds remarkably like the old-fashioned idea of "balance" that contextual healers have talked about for centuries. Many generations of contextual healers have called healthy bodies "balanced" because their functions seem to operate at just the right level. And they've called unhealthy bodies "out of balance" because their functions seem too strong or too weak. And they've claimed to *balance* unhealthy bodies by adjusting what now begin to look like context parameters, which might shift body functions from the dynamic extremes toward some more central point. Until contextual science came along, however, they had no scientific way to explain what they were doing.

On the other hand, classical scientists knew all about molecules, but they didn't know about distance from equilibrium. And being the guardians of science as they knew it, they called the balance principle "unscientific," and heaped scorn and contempt upon the contextual healers who practiced it. But what if those old-time contextual healers were simply noticing intuitively what contextual science has now placed in a clearer light, while classical scientists were mocking the balance idea simply because their unwavering focus on molecules hid it from their view?

Consider also that distance from equilibrium adjusts the relationship between the molecular system (the *stable* properties of the molecules) and the system's context (the *dynamic* properties of flowing matter and energy). Perhaps "health" exists when the system's stability and the context's dynamism strike a balance. Ice, after all, is solid because the molecular properties predominate. Steam is vaporous because the flowing energy of heat predominates. Water is fluid because the stable molecular attractions balance neatly against the dynamic flowing of contextual heat. Perhaps this is the essence of the Chinese idea of balancing *yin* and *yang*.[10]

The Emergence of Self-Organization

The old-time contextual healers also believed their adjustments were strengthening some sort of innate healing power, which earned them yet another measure of scorn. But perhaps they were once again noticing intuitively a property of nature that contextual science has only now begun to explain. The property I'm refer-ring to is *self-organization*.

Imagine scattering gravel willy-nilly on the head of a bass drum, then striking the drumhead with a mallet. Can you picture anything more calculated to create a random, disordered *mess?* Yet it doesn't create a mess as the photograph in Figure 1 shows."[11] Agitating gravel on a drumhead creates a beautiful pattern. This is an example of *self-organization* arising far from equilibrium.

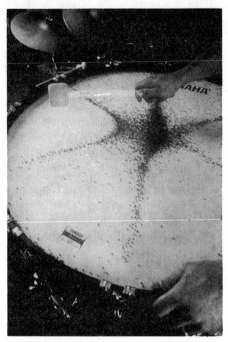

Figure 1. Pattern created by striking a drumhead covered with gravel.

This is called *self*-organization because the information that creates the pattern doesn't exist anywhere by itself. It can only emerge *spontaneously* when the conditions are right, with the main condition (supplied by the energy of the mallet) being a certain distance from equilibrium. There's no information about the pattern in the physical properties of the mallet. And there's no information about the pattern in the physical properties of the drumhead itself. The drummer isn't trying to *impose* the pattern by the force of his intellect or will, yet when he does nothing more than drive the drumhead away from equilibrium by striking it with the mallet, the pattern spontaneously appears.

In an example that's closer to our present interests, a biophysicist named Belousov was trying to build a test-tube model of the chemical reactions that cells go through when they make energy. As he fiddled with his solution, it surprised him by beginning to change colors in a clocklike rhythm. First it would be yellow, then it would be clear, then yellow, then clear—like a flashing traffic signal, only slower. Belousov was using the element cerium, which turns yellow when it's oxidized and clear when it's not. So he figured the reaction must be alternating rhythmically between cerium's oxidized and unoxidized states. He wrote a scientific paper on his discovery, but no journal would accept it. One editor even wrote to him that his "discovery" was quite impossible.[12]

The editor's problem was that he only knew molecules, and Belousov's rhythm also depends on the context. In fact, Belousov had to adjust a number of context parameters just to set the reaction up.[13] He had to stir the solution to keep it mixed; he had to adjust its temperature; and he had to adjust how fast the various chemicals got pumped in and out of the solution. "This experimental setup," Nicolis and Prigogine point out, "allows easy control over the distance from equilibrium."[14] And when the distance from equilibrium along the various parameters is *just right*, the rhythm spontaneously appears—a fact that has now been confirmed so many times that we can hardly dispute it. The molecules aren't inherently rhythmical (at least not at the tempo the solution assumes) and neither is the context, so the rhythmic behavior that appears when the two of them come together is *self*-organized, or spontaneous.[15]

In a more recent experiment, scientists tracked the rhythmic contractions of a segment of catgut that they'd placed in a solution. They used two methods to track the rhythms, and actually traced the results on paper where they could see the rhythms as wavy up-and-down lines. Once they'd established the catgut's basic rhythm, they changed one of its context parameters. They varied the amount of calcium in the solution, and as they did so, the catgut's rhythm changed in a very apparent way.[16] The calcium wasn't telling the catgut what rhythm to beat, and neither were the molecules the catgut was made from. The new rhythm emerged spontaneously from the *combination* of the molecular system and the particular setting of the calcium parameter, so it was *self*-organized—not imposed from the outside.

This, in essence, is what the old-time contextual healers used to do. They would adjust some parameter of the body's context and honestly expect the body's behavior to change as a result. And after a lot of experience, their adjustments would usually work (they claimed), even though the parameters they adjusted generally weren't *logically* connected to the changes they saw. So they blamed what they saw on the operation of an innate healing power, while the molecular scientists who opposed them said molecules simply don't behave that way. Yet the molecular scientists didn't understand distance from equilibrium, and they didn't understand how self-organized behavior can spontaneously emerge when distance from equilibrium is set just right. Is this another case of the contextual healers sensing intuitively something the classical scientists couldn't see because they mistakenly thought molecules were all that mattered?

Making a Difference Without Making Sense

I've been speaking abstractly about the body's "context parameters." It might be good to remind ourselves that our context parameters include all the things that define how we *interact* with our context: what we eat, drink, breathe, smell, see, hear, do, say, and think, plus structural constraints of various sorts. I discussed them earlier under four general headings: inflow, outflow, structure, and mind. Some parameters we adjust for ourselves; others may require the services of a trained healer. In any case, the basic idea is that adjusting these context parameters can change how our body behaves, with some changes making us sick while others make us well. This principle would explain all the recent talk about the relationships between diet and health, exercise and health, stress and health, and so on.

Most of the time, however, there's no logical connection between the nature of a parameter and the behavior it's supposed to affect any more than there's a logical connection between the pounding of the bass drum and the pattern it creates. Furthermore, you can't predict the outcome of an adjustment that's never been done before, even though you can reproduce it as often as you want once you've discovered it. As a consequence, context-related behavior changes can seem irrational and unexplainable in cause-and-effect terms, and the adjustments that produce them often seem too small to make such a difference, yet they clearly do.

For example, one of the most interesting phenomena in all of nature involves a species of amoeba called "slime mold." Slime mold amoebas live in large colonies. Each colony may include many thousands of individual amoebas, and when sufficient food exists, they each forage independently. But when the food supply runs out, one amoeba sends out a chemical signal that emits a cyclic, rhythmic beat, and the other amoebas move toward the signal in rhythmic waves.

When they converge, they undergo a remarkable transformation. They become a single body, with a "foot" that extends forward to inch them along toward some new area where food might exist. When they find such an area, they break up and once again forage individually until the next rhythmic signal comes along.[17]

This response has been observed many times. Yet imagine trying to predict it beforehand. You take an amoeba and a microscope—even a whole *colony* of amoebas and a microscope—and begin analyzing all the molecular details you can see. But nowhere will you see even the tiniest hint of the transformation that will take place when the food runs out. And although there's a certain general logic to the idea that hungry amoebas might gather together to go hunt for food, there's no cause-and-effect logic in the classical molecular sense. So it seems irrational and unreasonable, yet it's true.

A more relevant transformation apparently occurs in another amoeba—the one that causes amoebic dysentery. This transformation is related to the fact that only 10 percent of the people infected with the amoeba actually get sick. A number of years ago, researchers noticed that virulent amoebas (the ones that make us sick) can survive on a diet of finely ground rice, while benign amoebas die unless they get their usual diet of live, healthy bacteria. The researchers concluded from this that benign amoebas and virulent amoebas must be two separate strains, which they seemed to confirm when they analyzed the genetic makeup of the strains.

Then two other researchers tried to wean benign amoebas from bacteria to rice powder by feeding them a transition diet consisting of bacteria that had been weakened by radiation. By inserting this transition diet (which amounted to a gentle context adjustment), the researchers managed next to get the benign amoebas to live on rice powder—a circumstance that had killed benign amoebas before. But when they tested the genes of *these* benign amoebas, they found that they'd been transformed into the virulent strain! When they reversed the context adjustment (fed them healthy bacteria, in other words) the amoebas turned benign again.

Now, imagine analyzing all the molecular details of a benign amoeba and trying to predict that particular change. You couldn't do it any more than you could analyze a raindrop and predict a snowflake. Yet classical scientists insist on doing just that sort of thing. As a consequence, they have a hard time accepting the idea that benign amoebas can turn virulent and vice versa. "It's a stretch," one of them said, "to imagine how an organism can change its genes depending on its environment." Even one of the scientists who did the research says the process "seems to have some sort of magic in it."[18]

Yet it may simply be the magic of self-organization, which allows molecular systems to change their behavior when their context is changed. This experiment adds a new twist because the genes apparently changed as well. Yet gene adaptations aren't excluded by any known principle, and Nobel Prize-winning research by Barbara McClintock seems to confirm that genes actually can change.[19] Now researchers confidently talk about the "genetic stress response"[20] and the "SOS response,"[21] referring explicitly to the idea that genes may change when their context is changed. In one recent study, researchers even saw new genes appear for an "antifreeze protein" in fish that were exposed to water that was colder than what they'd been used to.[22]

In any case, we have in this amoeba example a single microorganism changing its behavior in a dramatic and important way just because its context changes. And when amoebas live inside of humans, their context is simply an extension of the context that we create for ourselves, which may explain intriguing differences like these:

> When [amoebic dysentery] struck white persons in South Africa, few symptoms resulted. The middle-class Indians, infected by the same organisms, suffered diarrhea and minor intestinal trouble, but the Bantu developed liver abscesses. The same amoeba, depending on racial and social factors, produced human reactions ranging from the negligible to death.[23]

Those differences are hard to explain from a purely molecular point of view, yet they fall neatly within both the new ideas of contextual science and the old-fashioned ideas of the contextual healers.

Maintaining the Rhythms of Life

When I was about nine years old, I used to go tubing down a canal with a friend. We would settle bottoms-down inside our inner tubes, ride them a half-mile or so down the canal, then jump out of the water and carry our tubes back upstream for another trip. We used to spend hours doing this, never realizing that we were illustrating a principle of physics.

I mentioned earlier the idea that the farther you go up a river, the farther from equilibrium the river's water gets. That same principle applies here. From the perspective of the canal's energy, our trips down-canal took us *toward* equilibrium, and our walks back up-canal took us *away* from equilibrium.

As far as our *own* internal energy is concerned, we were doing just the opposite. Our lazy rides down-canal let our bodies recuperate internal energy, while our walks back up-canal required that we expend it. By the same token, when you pushed the boulder uphill in our earlier example, you were giving internal energy to the boulder at the expense of your own, and you could have recuperated your internal energy by riding the boulder downhill, except you probably would have gotten squashed, which would have canceled any recuperative effect. But here we're talking about the flowing energy of the canal, and my friend and I, by moving in turns toward the canal's equilibrium and away from it, kept ourselves hovering around a *particular* distance from equilibrium—just as the body does.

The body does this hovering by coupling two kinds of chemical reactions: catabolic and anabolic. Catabolic reactions are like our trips *down* the canal. They use the system's internal energy—spend it, in a sense—in this case by breaking complex molecules apart. Anabolic reactions are like our trips *up* the canal. They recapture internal energy by building simple elements into complex molecules.[24] And, like our youthful trips up and down the canal, anabolic and catabolic reactions generally take turns so that molecules end up getting broken down, then reformed, then broken down again, then reformed, over and over again.

As these two kinds of reactions take their turns—one moving us toward equilibrium, the other moving us away from it—they *stabilize* the body in a fluctuating position around a *particular* distance from equilibrium. From the perspective of contextual science, being able to maintain a particular distance from equilibrium is *very* important, and this anabolic-catabolic partnership is one of the ways it happens in us.

The anabolic-catabolic partnership also means that the body produces and consumes its complex molecules in rhythmic, up-and-down cycles. Some of those cycles correspond to our daily rhythm of waking and sleeping; others pulse to their own shorter or longer beats. Some cycles are synchronized with other cycles, while others are offset in precise and particular ways. Many such rhythms exist, weaving themselves into an intricate and dynamic *pattern in time* that has a lot to do with how we think and feel.

For example, PMS involves disturbed rhythms.[25] It is, after all, a cyclical disorder. Yet disturbed rhythms also show up in cancer[26] and a host of other chronic illnesses that *aren't* obviously cyclical.[27] In their book *From Clocks to Chaos: The Rhythms of Life,* Leon Glass and Michael Mackey call these "dynamical diseases," which they define as "variations of rhythms outside of normal limits, or appearance of new rhythms where none existed previously."[28]

Rhythms arise spontaneously in far-from-equilibrium systems that replace the energy they lose. They emerge from the coupling of (1) processes that expend internal energy and (2) processes that restore it. It is literally true that far-from-equilibrium systems like the body must pulse with the rhythm of this coupling or they will die.

In 1960, a medical researcher named Crammer wrote about rhythmic processes in disease and complained that "this knowledge does not seem to have penetrated clinical medicine."[29] In 1963, a researcher named Reimann noted that the link between rhythm and disease "is received skeptically and the subject is confused."[30] As recently as 1988, Glass and Mackey reported that "this view is not currently popular among physicians or medical researchers."[31] Medicine disregards rhythms because they depend on context parameters, which medicine's classical perspective ignores. Contextual healers, on the other hand, have talked about rhythms and cycles for centuries. And now they're part of the new scientific perspective that Ilya Prigogine and the other contextual scientists have introduced.

Energy Transport and the Spine

Perhaps no contextual healing discipline has borne more mocking than chiropractic. For example, a medical researcher named Edmund Crelin once tested the chiropractic theory of subluxations by isolating the spine from a cadaver, mounting it in a vice, and then artificially "subluxating" it to see if he could get the bones of the spine to "pinch" the nerve. When the bones wouldn't pinch the nerve unless he practically destroyed the spine, he concluded that chiropractic couldn't possibly be valid.[32]

Based on this research, the president of the National Council Against Health Fraud made light of chiropractors as follows:

> Instead of the scientific response of attempting to replicate [Crelin's] research, the ACA [American Chiropractic Association] wrote a tirade of verbiage, concluding that his work was invalid because it was done on cadavers. In fact, Crelin states [that] the absence of a reflex response in a dead body should make subluxations easier to produce. Faced with this evidence, a true-believing chiropractor once remarked to me that the reason Crelin had failed to demonstrate the chiropractic hypothesis was that he worked with cada-

vers in which the innate Life Force was no longer present![33]

This comment reflects the classical position that a cadaver and a living body are more or less the same. But from the perspective of contextual science, the cadaver has ceased interacting with its context so that it's no longer far from equilibrium. Practically speaking, a cadaver is *at* equilibrium, which is why it's dead.

In living bodies, nerves work only because we maintain ourselves far from equilibrium. We use our internal energy to create within our nerves a polarity, or a difference in electrical charge, similar to the one that exists in a battery. This polarity comes about when far-from-equilibrium processes sustain a high concentration of potassium inside our nerve cells juxtaposed against a low concentration of potassium in the fluids that surround them.[34] This difference can't exist at equilibrium because there's no internal energy to sustain it. As a consequence, the polarity that nerves rely on can't exist in a cadaver.

The protesting chiropractor said the research wasn't valid because the innate Life Force is no longer present in a cadaver. Was he truly off the mark?

I mentioned earlier Hermann Haken's feeling that the laser principle may somehow underlie the operation of our nerves. If so, it may take the form of a related phenomenon called the "soliton wave."

One of the first people to notice a soliton wave was a Scottish engineer named John Scott Russell, who saw one in August of 1834. He was riding his horse down the Union Canal near Edinburgh alongside a boat being drawn by two horses. When the boat suddenly stopped, Russell noticed that the water being pushed forward by the prow of the boat didn't dissipate as waves usually do.

Instead, this wave continued to roll forward down the canal in what he described as "a rounded, smooth and well-defined heap of water, which continued its course along the channel apparently without change of form or diminution of speed."[35]

The "heap of water" was about thirty feet long and a foot or so high. Russell followed it for about two miles before he lost it in the windings of the canal. Most waves fall apart in a flurry of foam. This one, for as long as Russell watched it, never lost its basic shape.

Soliton waves must be sustained by their context in a very particular way. To be specific, the energy that leaves them must be balanced by the energy that comes into them.[36] This balancing keeps them far from equilibrium (like my youthful tubing trips up and down the canal), and being far from equilibrium allows them to sustain both their energy and their shape.

More than a few scientists now propose that soliton waves in the body "play functional roles in vital processes of energy transport."[37] They may be how energy gets transported down protein molecules, for example.[38] And they may be how nerve energy gets transmitted down the spine.[39]

Soliton waves, like laser beams, organize energy so that it becomes focused and useful. To see what an immense difference this focusing makes, consider this comparison. The energy of an ordinary light bulb diffuses in all directions and quickly ceases to be useful. Yet when we adjust a few context parameters and, in particular, when we constrain the light energy within a precisely shaped cavity, it suddenly emerges as a single wavetrack whose length may reach tens of thousands of miles. This is the laser beam. Furthermore, when we slightly increase input power to an ordinary light bulb, the output power (the intensity of the light) increases by an equally slight amount. But when we slightly increase the input power to a tuned laser device, the output power increases dramatically.[40]

One of these two energy principles—the principle of diffusion exemplified by ordinary light bulbs or the principle of focus exemplified by laser beams and soliton waves—empowers our body. Classical science acknowledges the principle of diffusion; only contextual science explains them both. If we conclude that we operate by the principle of focus exemplified by laser beams and soliton waves, then we must also conclude that we exist by virtue of certain context parameters that must be set just so. And if we can generalize from a laser device, one of those context parameters is structural—"the existence of a particular cavity structure . . . that functions as an 'ordering principle.' "[41] Might that not describe the spine?

If so, a "subluxation" wouldn't have to physically pinch the nerve to have an effect. It would be sufficient simply to distort the shape of the cavity that surrounds it.

Reproducibility vs. Rationality

The final parallel between contextual healers and contextual scientists is that neither group cares about linear cause-and-effect explanations. They value reproducibility above rationality.

I introduced this idea earlier when I said that you can't predict snowflakes by analyzing raindrops. In other words, if you don't already know that snowflakes exist, there's no logical way to derive them analytically from raindrops because the only thing raindrops and snowflakes have in common is water molecules, and there's more than water molecules involved. In this sense, the idea that snowflakes might emerge from water molecules is irrational, meaning that it's not subject to ordinary cause-and-effect logic, and it can't be predicted beforehand.

But irrational doesn't mean random or arbitrary, because snowflakes are absolutely reproducible. If we adjust our context parameters just so and apply them to raindrops, we'll get snowflakes every time, and the first time would necessarily be a wonderful and glorious surprise.

Classical science, on the other hand, demands rationality. It requires that things be predictable beforehand, and that they be entirely explainable by logical pathways that go from cause to effect in unbroken straight lines. Classical science abhors surprises, particularly if no one can explain them even after they've been analyzed until there's nothing more to see.

This has always presented classical science with a dilemma: what do you do with unexplained surprises? A common response has been to deny them in the fashion of the skeptical editor who wrote to Belousov that his rhythmical chemical reaction was quite impossible.

The developer of the laser principle experienced much the same thing: "I found myself in opposition to all previously published papers and therefore asked some of the experts whether such behavior could occur. And they told me: No, this cannot be the case."[42]

More to our present point, today's classical scientists face the surprising discovery that low-level electromagnetic radiation of the sort we experience from electric power lines can profoundly affect our health. The levels are so low that their effects "do not appear to originate in classical processes of events,"[43] meaning that classical science can't explain them. As a consequence, classical

scientists often deny that they're real. Yet soliton waves
in protein molecules very likely *would* be affected by
radiation of that tiny magnitude.[44] Is low-level electromagnetic radiation therefore a context parameter that
we should learn to adjust?

I once read a story of two classical scientists musing
over Joseph Priestley's discovery of oxygen in 1774. "I
wonder," one said to the other, "what people breathed
before then."

There's humor in this story because things *do* exist
before classical scientists discover them. Surprises ought
to be the essence of science—perhaps even its goal. The
nonclassical scientists who study complex, context-dependent behavior have learned to appreciate surprises
because they so often see "results that violate the standard intuition of practitioners,"[45] meaning results that
classical science can't predict. By one recent description,
far-from-equilibrium systems like the body represent "a
mathematical version of the twilight zone."[46] Their behavior so often runs "directly counter to normal human
intuition"[47] that "nonanalytic behavior appears to be more
the rule than the exception in the social and medical sciences."[48]

As we seek to heal this complex, context-dependent
body of ours, must we *truly* require that its responses be
rational to our own limited minds? Or is it enough that
we be able to faithfully reproduce them? Classical science
demands rationality. Contextual healing accepts reproducibility. This is one of the reasons why the two ways of
looking at things sometimes don't get along.

4

The Coupling of Body and Mind

Few things tax classical scientific logic more than the apparent coupling between the body and the mind. The body is molecular; the mind is not. By what principle could one possibly affect the other?

Classical scientists once coped with this perplexing coupling by denying it altogether. That became more difficult in the early 1950s when medical researchers were testing a drug called chlorpromazine. They'd hoped chlorpromazine might reduce the shock that often follows surgery, but they found instead a totally unexpected effect. When they gave the drug to patients who happened to be psychotic, the patients got better. The drug, it appeared, was altering a state of mind.

Other researchers soon confirmed the effect, and it sent a ripple of shock through the medical community. It suggested not only that molecules could affect the mind, but that mental illnesses may have physical causes, which few people had ever supposed. Today, nearly forty years later, most scientists, classical or otherwise, accept the idea that mental illnesses may have physical causes, although the mechanisms connecting the two are by no means clear.[1]

Even more challenging for classical science is the idea that the connection may also operate in the opposite direction—that physical illnesses may have some basis in the mind. This isn't a new idea. Contextual healers have generally accepted it, and even medical doctors have proposed it from time to time. In 1796, for example, a physician named William Falconer wrote a book called *The Influence of the Passions upon Disorders of the Body*, but it wasn't well received.[2] Even today, it seems much easier to believe that physical causes have mental effects than the other way around.

Evidence of a Mind-Body Coupling

The problem is the *coupling*. By what possible means can mental events bring about physical effects? Mental events are insubstantial, almost ghostlike. We can't measure them, and they don't represent any known physical force. Yet they appear to influence, and to be influenced by, physical events—molecular activities in our cells—that supposedly respond only to physical forces according to precise physical laws. It's hard to imagine how this coupling of two such different domains occurs.

Yet it obviously does. Imagine, for example, a male moose bellowing during mating season. Experts in animal mating used to call the bellowing a scare tactic for keeping competing males away. But then researchers at Cambridge University discovered that the bellowing of male animals triggers ovulation in females.[3] The bellowing strikes the female as vibrating air molecules. The ovulation that results is a complex endocrine process. A coupling between air molecules and endocrine hormones obviously exists, and if mooses have minds, that is where the coupling would logically appear to be.

Perhaps mooses don't have minds, but we humans do, and a similar coupling occurs in us. When men and women do nothing more than see one another, their circulating sex hormones often undergo immediate and significant shifts. What we see is only quantum packets of light, yet particular patterns of them, transformed somehow within the mind, have power to stir us in molecular ways.[4]

Researchers asked actors to assume the facial expressions of anger, disgust, joy, and so on. As the actors did so, their bodies responded. Heart rates went up for expressions of anger, fear, and sadness; down for expressions of disgust. Finger temperatures soared in response to anger, rose just a little for happiness and sadness, and dropped for disgust, fear, and surprise.[5]

When researchers ask subjects to imagine pain, their imagining triggers the body's natural pain-killing chemicals.[6] We may trigger the same pain killers just by witnessing someone else's pain.[7] When experimental subjects see a flashing light, certain patterns of electrical activity appear in their brains; when asked to *imagine* the flashing light, the same patterns appear.[8]

A coupling obviously exists through which the mind affects the body. And the coupling just as obviously involves more than molecules, which creates another circumstance like the ones we discussed in the last chapter. Because of its purely molecular focus, classical science generally disregards the mind-body coupling and criticizes the contextual healers who insist not only that it exists, but that it can profoundly affect our health. Can principles of contextual science explain this mind-body coupling?

Information as a Context Parameter

Let's assume, to begin with, that the mind deals with information and that *sensory information* is one of the body's context parameters. In that case, we should be able to vary sensory information along some dimension and create reproducible changes in the body's behavior. Researchers at the University of California at Berkeley did precisely this in an animal study by implanting tiny electrodes in the brains of rabbits. They arranged the electrodes in rows and columns in the part of the brain that handles smelling. They withheld food from the rabbits and then exposed them to odors. Through the electrodes, they observed the patterns of electrical activity the odors triggered.

The patterns were rhythmic. The details of the patterns depended on the particular odor the rabbits were exposed to, but in general they came in two basic categories: synchronized and desynchronized. When the rabbits knew the odor, the researchers saw *synchronized* rhythms. When the rabbits didn't know the odor, the researchers saw *desynchronized* rhythms.[9] Desynchronized rhythms are "an electrographic correlate of 'alertness.' "[10]

The parameter in this case would be something like the "surprise value" of the information. Unsurprising information creates one pattern of rhythmic activity; surprising information creates another. And a "transition boundary" separates the two that is as precise as the boundary that separates raindrops and snowflakes.[11]

For information to affect the body as a context parameter, it must function somehow as energy. Yet energy has a real physical existence, while information—the intelligible *message*—seems as insubstantial as thoughts. How can information act as if it were energy? The answer, it turns out, is that information is essentially a form of energy.

This insight came out of radar research during World War II. During the early months of the war, allied gun crews were having a hard time shooting down German bombers. Their radar signals kept coming back fuzzy and filled with interference, or noise. They needed a radar system that could separate the information *from* the noise, so researchers began working to develop one.

They were quite successful, it turned out. Allied gunners had been hitting about 10 percent of their targets before the researchers began their work. After the researchers improved the radar system, the gunners hit 50 percent of their targets.[12]

To separate the information from the noise, the researchers used complicated mathematics based on concepts Albert Einstein won the Nobel Prize for in 1921. Shortly after the war, Claude Shannon published two papers reconceptualizing the mathematics and showing how messages could be sent most efficiently from one place to another. The main thing Shannon did was define mathematically and precisely the word *information*. His definition applies to messages in any form: chemical, mechanical, electrical, or whatever.

As people came to understand Shannon's mathematics, a most surprising fact became apparent. His *information* equations and the equations for certain aspects of thermodynamic *energy* were virtually identical. This suggested, at the very least, "a powerful analogy between energy and information."[13] Perhaps this "powerful analogy" could allow us to count information as one of our context parameters.[14]

Information as an Energy Principle

To see why energy and information are in many respects the same, imagine a jumble of alphabet blocks. To line them up in a row, you must expend energy. To spell random words, you must expend more energy. To spell sensible sentences, you must expend more energy still. In a very direct sense, you may measure the amount of energy you've invested in those blocks by measuring the quality of the information they express.

This is not a trivial relationship, nor is it coincidental. Scientists calculate, for example, a minimum amount of chemical energy needed to join two amino acids. But when the body joins amino acids to form proteins, it expends ten to twenty times that minimum amount:

> It would seem at first sight that nature has developed a method of protein synthesis that is wildly extravagant in its use of energy. However, in return for this expenditure the organism gets one of its basic requirements. The amino acids are linked together *in a definite order.*[15]

This, as you can see, is the "alphabet block" principle: the energy expended equals the quality of the information expressed. The body uses this molecular information to direct the energy processes of our cells. Therefore

> one may loosely think of information as a special kind of energy required for the work of establishing order. . . . If biological order is as close as we can come to the essence of life, information management must be the central purpose for which living things mobilize energy.[16]

By these new insights, molecules become a *kind* of information. This is why I described genes as containing information, and why Franklin Harold (author of the quote I just cited) calls information management "the central purpose for which living things mobilize energy."

Molecular information directs our physiological processes. To see how, imagine dropping a marble into a stainless steel mixing bowl. It settles to the bottom, of course, and that *settling* is precisely what chemical reactions do. They proceed until they reach a "bottom" that's identical, in principle, to the bottom of the mixing bowl. It's the configuration where all the useful energy is gone—the state of equilibrium we've been talking about, the state where all activity stops and everything becomes still. Put another way, spontaneous chemical reactions always proceed *toward* equilibrium—from higher internal energy toward lower internal energy. They can't proceed away from equilibrium any more than marbles can roll up the sides of mixing bowls, air can flow into balloons, or ashes can *un*burn into logs.

Now, imagine the same marble sitting perched on a tiny platform about an inch below the mixing bowl's rim. It *could* roll down to the bottom, but it doesn't, because the platform stands in its way. We have to give the marble a little push to get it going. This image represents the fact that chemical reactions that *could* proceed toward equilibrium don't always do it, because some chemical equivalent of that little platform gets in their way. They need a little push—a little *activation energy* to get them going—after which they will proceed nicely on their own. The "activation energy" that gets a campfire going, for example, is the match.

The point is, all sorts of chemical reactions that *could* happen in the body don't happen because they need a little activation energy to get them going. And this is what the genes provide. But they provide it in a very particular way. They provide the *information equivalent* of activation energy—by making *enzymes*.

Enzymes are complex molecules with very particular shapes. They use their particular shapes to attract molecules and juxtapose them into precise spatial configurations. So juxtaposed, the molecules spontaneously react as if, so to speak, they had been lit by a match. In other words, enzymes provide the *equivalent* of activation energy, yet all they really do is *arrange the interacting molecules in physical space*.

As you can see, that arranging in physical space is the alphabet-block principle. It's as if the interacting molecules were letters and the enzymes were arranging them in words and sentences. Yet the effect of that arranging is to trigger a chemical reaction that otherwise wouldn't happen without a shot of genuine activation energy. Functionally, information (the spatial arrangement) and activation energy are the same.

And this is how our genes set off some reactions rather than others. They make an enzyme, and the enzyme acts as a messenger, with its message being expressed as a sentencelike configuration of molecules, which then spontaneously reacts.

This is why you can find enzymes described in scientific literature like this:

> One can regard enzyme catalysis as a clever trick that uses *information* . . . to overcome the activation energy barrier.[17]

Or like this:

> The precision of complementary fit between [the molecules] and [the enzyme] provides the

thermodynamic basis for the *cognitive* as well as the catalytic functions of enzymes.[18]

Information and Adaptation

Let's assume with Franklin Harold, then, that "information management must be the central purpose for which living things mobilize energy."[19] We manage two kinds of information: (1) information that comes into us from our context and (2) information that exists within our genes. The two kinds of information—contextual and genetic—*interact*, which takes a coupling device, and that coupling device is the mind. Our body couples with its context *by way of* the mind.

On the other hand, the body also couples the mind with *its* context. The mind receives information about its context by way of the body's sense organs. The mind acts *upon* its context by way of the body's capacities for action and effort. From this view, the body becomes the instrument of the mind rather than the other way around.

In either case, the function of the mind may be generally expressed as follows: it is a coupling device through which the reactions of our cells may *integrate* with the peculiarities of our circumstances. This we call *adapting*.

We adapt, for example, in space. Within a certain part of the brain, the cells respond to a number of sensory "modes"—sound, sight, touch, and so on. What's more, they appear to have what we might call "geographical assignments." A cell that responds to a touch from the rear also responds to a sound from the rear, and so on. Taken together, these cells apparently form a three-dimensional "map" that orients us in space.[20]

Sometimes this orienting in space can border on the miraculous. Back in the 1890s, a psychologist named G.

M. Stratton invented a set of prism goggles. The goggles created the interesting effect of reversing everything: the floor appeared where the ceiling should have been, the right side of the room switched to the left, and vice versa. Stratton put on the goggles and tried to walk around. After struggling for some time, a most surprising thing happened: the world suddenly righted itself. Now, when Stratton took the goggles off, the world he saw *without them* was upside down![21]

For this sort of adapting, information from our surroundings must pass through our mind to our cells. This takes some rather complex coupling that links information on one end to energy processes on the other. We may imagine that the information-based couplings of our mind are somehow different from the energy-based couplings of our body, but they're not:

> There is no fundamental difference between regulatory and sensory communications, even though one mode looks inward and the other looks outward. Both require a cell to recognize *a change in some significant parameter* and respond appropriately.[22]

An Act of Conscious Choice

So far in this chapter, I've tried to show that the principles of contextual science give us some useful ideas for understanding how our mind affects our health. They show that information, which seems insubstantial, can interact with molecules as long as some sort of coupling exists. A major part of that coupling, I'm suggesting, exists within what we call "the mind."

This is only a small piece of a very large puzzle, however, and I don't know that I can go much beyond it. For example, I experience the fact that *I* perceive this insubstantial information. Yet who, or what, am *I*. Sometimes I understand the information; sometimes I don't. What, precisely, is *understanding?* And based on what I understand, I *feel.* My feelings seem to depend on molecules, because scientists can manipulate my molecules and alter how I feel.[23] Yet if I weep for my child's pain, or for the joy of a relationship healed, something more than molecules is involved, and I don't know that any *scientific* principle can tell me what it is.

I also *choose*, and this is the heart of the matter. For choices have consequences, and among those consequences are illness and health. When we adjust our context parameters, we are *choosing* to be healthy or ill. And one of those context parameters is the mind.

So I want to discuss how we adjust our mind, although I'll have to depart from contextual science to do it. I'll be speculating, to be honest, although I hope to do it sensibly and based on a reasonable understanding of the facts.

First of all, I suggest that we must literally *choose* to couple with our context—that mental coupling is not something that happens by chance. Genuine mental coupling is active. It involves *moving* within our context, probing it, testing it, exploring it with the full range of our faculties. And we must *choose* to do it.

Imagine G. M. Stratton just putting on his prism goggles. He looks through them and sees what must surely be a very confusing sight. At some precise moment, he steps into the confusion. The decision to take that step *initiates* the coupling. If he had chosen not to initiate the coupling (had he been afraid, for example), that marvelous adapting would not have taken place.

Scientists once raised two kittens in darkness, so they remained blind. Then they introduced the kittens into the light, but each under a different circumstance. They harnessed one kitten to a basket, then put the other kitten *in* the basket, so the first kitten pulled the second kitten around the room. The kitten in the basket remained blind. The kitten pulling the basket developed sight, because it alone achieved the coupling.[24]

Scientists at the Smith-Kettlewell Institute of Visual Science in San Francisco connected a small TV camera through a computer to four hundred tiny skin stimulators—pointy instruments that electrically stimulate a spot of skin. They arranged the stimulators in a 20 x 20 grid, placed the grid on the back of a wheelchair, then had blind people sit in the wheelchair leaning back against the grid. They then pointed the TV camera at various objects, and the computer translated the camera's image into a pattern of dots pressed by the grid into the blind person's back.

The blind people literally *saw*, though in somewhat modified form. The grid stimulated their sense of touch, but their brain transformed the touch signals into what amounted to a *visual* image. This is called "sensory substitution," and though the touch impressions came from their back, the image they "saw" appeared in front of them—within the space scanned by the camera.

But to "see" in this fashion, the blind people had to operate the camera themselves. If someone else moved the camera, they experienced nothing more than tickles on their back. Only when they accepted the camera themselves and actively explored with it did the impressions become "visual" and correctly placed in space. Only a true *multisensory* coupling—a combining of the touch information from the grid and the muscular feedback from their active exploring with the camera— let their brains see what was really going on.[25]

In all such instances, some precise moment of coupling exists, a moment that we achieve, it appears, by allowing ourselves, or willing ourselves, to step into a circumstance that we don't understand.[26]

How Events Gain Their Meaning

We don't receive information pure, however. We interpret our present circumstances in light of our past experiences, which reside within us as what we might call "working memories." These working memories become an inner context for our present experiences—a particular bias, or an anticipation of future experiences—and they determine, in large measure, what our present experiences mean to us.[27]

For example, our working memories apparently account for the principle called "classical conditioning." The famous Russian physiologist Ivan Pavlov discovered classical conditioning when he got dogs to salivate to a bell by ringing the bell and exposing them to meat at the same time. The dogs apparently developed working memories that linked the bell with the anticipation of meat.

Another famous example of classical conditioning is John Watson's thoughtless experiment with an eleven-month-old boy who came to be known as "little Albert." As little Albert sat on the floor, Watson's assistant placed a white rat in front of him. Albert reached for it, and Watson, standing just behind him, struck a steel bar with a hammer. Albert jumped, fell forward, and began to whimper.

A week later they repeated the process, then again six more times. By now Albert would cry and try to crawl away the instant the rat appeared. He also feared rabbits, and showed the same reaction even to the white beard of a Santa Claus mask. Watson was training Albert's "working memories" in a cruel and insensitive way.[28]

Addiction, it appears, also involves working memories. After people use a drug for a while, their body starts compensating even before they take it.[29] For example, as soon as a heroin addict sees a needle, or runs into one of his drug-using buddies, or finds himself in a situation where he's used drugs before, he begins to experience cravings, apparently as a consequence of *conditioned* physiological responses. As one scientist put it, an addict's body compensates, not only for the physical presence of the drug, but also in response to "drug associated cues"[30]— sights, sounds, smells, etc., that the addict has experienced as part of his drug taking.

People also associate medical drugs with certain "cues." They take them in certain settings (hospitals, doctors offices) with particular apparatuses (syringes, pill bottles) in the presence of particular people (doctors, nurses). Could the *medical setting* itself provoke side effects—as a classical conditioning effect created by its association with the taking of drugs?

A recent pilot study suggests that it may. Twenty women who received chemotherapy in a hospital setting eventually came to experience the posttreatment side effects—reduced immunity and nausea—*before* their treatments. They weren't just imagining these effects. They were physiological—genuine drug side effects—even though the women hadn't yet taken the drugs. One review of the study concluded, "After repeatedly experiencing the immune-suppressing effects of chemotherapy in the distinctive hospital environment, cancer patients may undergo immunity dips triggered merely by a return to the hospital." Their working memories were making them sick.[31]

We don't have to rely on scientific evidence to know that working memories affect us. We've all experienced them personally. When I was a child, my mother fed our family lunch-meat sandwiches while we were waiting in a smelly garage for our car to get fixed. I got sick and threw up. Even today, lunch meat evokes memories of that event, including the nausea I felt. Nausea, for me, is the "meaning" of lunch meat, yet it has little to do with the lunch meat itself.[32]

I once spotted what I thought was a full carton of milk on the kitchen counter. By the time I realized it was empty, I'd already lifted it so forcefully that I'd smashed it into the underside of the kitchen cabinets that were hanging directly above. I had lifted the anticipations of my working memories, not the carton itself.

Brain scientist Karl Pribram points out that it's almost impossible for us to step onto a stopped escalator without it seeming to move. This is because our "working memories" of escalators cause us to expect movement, which we actually compensate for before it happens. Then, when the escalator doesn't move, our compensating gets expressed anyway, which we experience as a shifting of the escalator, even though it's perfectly still.[33]

Everything we perceive passes through these working memories. We experience only what they reveal to us. Whether or not the word *Tzultak'a* means anything to you depends on whether or not your working memories include it.[34] Events are no different than words in this regard.

Active mental coupling is our means of adjusting our working memories. If they're misinforming us, actively coupling with our context will eventually find it out. Active coupling requires that we keep an open mind, however—that we hold our interpretations tentative, and remain willing, through exploring, to check them out.

Motivated to Explore

We seem naturally inclined to do this. Even day-old infants couple with their surroundings. Within hours of birth, they look eagerly about, actively exploring. Researchers once began ringing a pleasant bell each time day-old infants turned to the right. The infants became more active and moved their head from side to side as if trying to figure out what was going on. They appeared at some point to "catch on," and from then on turned regularly to the right as if willing the bell to ring. When the researchers began ringing the bell for a leftward turn, the infants experimented again, and learned to turn to the left.[35]

Researchers once put rats in a cage equipped with a running wheel and a drinking spout. The spout gave no water unless the rats first ran in the wheel, which they quickly learned to do. Then the researchers reversed the connection, so that if the rats wanted to run in the wheel, they had to drink from the spout. The rats explored until they figured out the new relationship, and then set about drinking in order to run.

In one sense the researchers were controlling the rats, yet the rats ended up drinking and running whenever they wanted. What the experimenters made uncertain, the rats learned to control.[36]

The key to their learning was their exploring—their active *coupling* with their context—which all normal rats seem eagerly inclined to do. Put a normal rat in territory it's never seen before, and you'll see it sniff, and probe, and scurry from area to area, apparently exploring for exploring's sake.[37] When researchers train rats to follow a particular pathway to food and then open a new pathway to the same food, the rats just as often choose the new pathway, for no apparent reason other than to explore it.[38]

Scientists have discovered certain "pleasure centers" in the brain that trigger wonderful feelings. To study these pleasure centers, they probe animal brains with tiny electrodes until they find spots that the animals enjoy having stimulated. Sometimes they'll wire the centers with electrodes connected to tiny levers, so the animals can stimulate themselves, and they measure how powerful the pleasure is by counting how often the lever gets pushed.

In one experiment, scientists wired a particularly potent pleasure center in this fashion and gave rats free access to the lever. The rats stimulated themselves as if they could hardly get enough of it. Meanwhile, the scientists recorded on tape the exact pattern of each rat's pushes.

Then they played the patterns back. The rats experienced again the very pattern they had just produced for themselves, except this time they experienced it disconnected from any act of their own. And they tried to escape it, as if being subjected to pain. Obviously the self-initiated act of producing the pleasure was an inseparable part of the pleasure itself.[39]

These experiments show animal and human subjects doing two things: (1) coupling actively with their environment and (2) learning through this coupling to produce effects. Day-old infants who ring a bell by turning their head are producing an effect. Rats who drink water to release a running wheel, or who press levers to feel a buzz in their brain, are producing an effect. When behavioral psychologists "condition" pigeons to play ping pong for food, the pigeons—not the psychologists—end up producing the effects.

Robert W. White calls this "effectance," and claims that we're intrinsically motivated to achieve it. It is "what the sensory-neuro-muscular system wants to do when it is not occupied with homeostatic business."[40] Once we deal with our inner environment, he's saying, we turn eagerly to our outer environment, driven by a natural inclination to explore ways to produce effects.

A Sense of Uncontrollability

Why, then, would choosing to couple even be an issue? Why would anyone *not* choose to couple when the exploring it opens up to us seems to give us so much pleasure? The answer, apparently, has to do with our working memories. They can lead us to conclude that we're somehow helpless—that we're not able to produce effects.

Scientists create this state of helplessness in animals as Watson created Albert's helplessness: by exposing them to unpleasant experiences that they can't control—a series of random shocks, a forced swim in cold water, and so on. If the unpleasant circumstance doesn't last too long, or if the animal has a chance to escape, it stays normal, meaning that it remains eager to explore anything new. But if the uncertainty goes on beyond a certain point, the animal undergoes what we would call, in humans, "a personality shift." If we now place it in a new circumstance, it no longer seeks to explore.[41]

In the language of the people who study these things, the animal has learned "uncontrollability," meaning that it no longer feels able to control what happens to it. This is what we mean when we say it has become "helpless." Placed in other adverse situations, it no longer tries to escape. Faced with novelty, it no longer couples with its context and actively seeks to explore.[42]

At the same time, helpless animals undergo dramatic physiological shifts. Certain hormones get overproduced;

others get underproduced. Hormones whose cycles are normally linked now become unlinked, and vice versa. These hormone shifts become a virtual fingerprint for this helpless state. By facilitating certain behaviors while suppressing others, they promote both the personality shift and the animal's enduring unwillingness to explore.[43]

Such shifts appear in many animal species. When lizards fight, the losers may turn brown, become depressed, and die.[44] Dogs who are shocked in a situation they can't escape from end up not trying to escape at all, even when they can.[45] Humans may experience helplessness during chronic unemployment,[46] in "posttraumatic stress,"[47] or when widows and widowers die of a "broken heart."[48]

Anatomy of an Illusion

Now, let's consider the practical effects of this illusion of helplessness. In one ingenious experiment, subjects sat in a swivel chair facing three small model rooms: one to the left, one to the right, and one straight ahead. Only one of the rooms was normal. The other two were distorted, one with a left wall twice the size of the right, the other with a ceiling twice the size of the floor. Both distorted rooms obviously had slanted walls and odd angles connecting them, but thanks to clever designing that followed principles of perspective, all of the rooms, viewed from the swivel chair, looked the same.

Now, imagine a subject seated in the swivel chair. He receives a pointer and is asked to touch a "bug" painted on the left wall of one of the rooms. He tries, but fails, because the room he's exploring is the one with the oversized left wall. He reaches farther and farther, chuckling with amazement, yet still fails to reach the "bug." Now he is asked to touch a similar "bug" on the right wall, with opposite results. He overreaches this time, striking the back wall, and only by withdrawing the pointer with great care and uncertainty can he eventually strike the proper spot. After several trials, the subject suddenly sees the room as it is, with the oversized left wall, and the odd angles forming the corners. Now, with adjusted perspective, he easily performs all the tasks asked of him.

At this point he is invited to inspect the other two rooms. Amazingly, he sees them also with oversized left walls and odd-angled corners, even though neither of them is actually that shape! Only after poking around in all three rooms can the subject come to perceive things as they are.[49]

The subjects in this distorted-room experiment coupled *visually* with the rooms the moment they sat in the swivel chair, yet they still couldn't see that they were deceived. They had to couple physically and visually *at the same time*, which took poking around with the pointer while keeping their eyes and their minds wide open. If they'd refused to poke, or if they'd denied the evidence of the pointer because it contradicted the evidence of their eyes, they would never have known the truth.

Now suppose they'd approached this experience with an illusion of helplessness. Suppose their working memories had included the idea—and they had accepted it—that they were threatened by such experiences and were powerless to ignore their fear or affect the threat. Would they have coupled in the same eager fashion? Would they have chuckled at the contradictions and worked curiously to resolve them? Or would they not have avoided the coupling and postured themselves to counter the threat they mistakenly perceived?

Suppose, by the same token, that we feel helpless as we face some of our real-life challenges. Will we then couple with them eagerly and wholeheartedly? Will we laugh at the contradictions we experience and work curiously to resolve them? Or will we avoid the coupling and posture ourselves to counter the threat we mistakenly perceive?

Walter Rudolf Hess once noted that he could provoke what looked like normal behaviors in animals by giving them drugs. "The only abnormality," he said, "consists in the fact that this behavior occurs inappropriately, i.e., not in conformity with the actual environmental situation."[50] Wouldn't that "abnormality"—behavior that occurs inappropriately—also be our consequence for failing to couple actively and eagerly with our context? And could that be the condition we call stress?

Adjusting Our States of Mind

We speak of "states of mind." Our English language gives us many names for them. Some of the names are positive—curiosity, eagerness, happiness, playfulness. Others are negative—anger, frustration, discouragement, resentment. Don't the positive names describe the state of open and active coupling? And don't the negative names describe the uncoupled state of helplessness and fear? And is it possible that by completely and wholeheartedly coupling with our context—even when we're afraid—we might transform our state of mind?

Now, assuming from this that we can "adjust our state of mind" by mentally coupling or uncoupling with our context, how might that adjusting affect the body? I mentioned earlier the rabbit study in which the researchers found that familiar odors and unfamiliar odors evoke two different kinds of rhythmic patterns in the rabbits' brains. Could we perhaps say that the rabbits were *bored* by the familiar odors and that they were *curious* about the new ones? "Bored" and "curious" are names for states of mind. And if "bored" and "curious" produce their own unique rhythmic patterns, wouldn't all of those other states of mind—positive and negative—generate their own rhythmic patterns as well?

Rhythms are of no small consequence in the body. They literally organize and integrate our physiological processes.[51] They keep us "in step," in a sense, like the drum section of a marching band.

I mentioned earlier that some scientists think the weak electromagnetic fields put out by power lines may make us sick by disturbing the soliton energy that powers our proteins and nerves. Could the rhythmic fields of our negative emotions perhaps do much the same thing?

This is conjecture, of course. Yet it is plausible conjecture, and I mean nothing more by it than to show that contextual science, coupled with certain common-sense observations, gives us some interesting alternatives to the purely molecular approach of classical science. And those interesting alternatives again seem to give at least some scientific foundation to contextual-healing ideas that were once discredited and condemned—in this case, the idea that our mind can affect our health.[52]

5

Explaining Cancer: Context or Genes?

My goal so far has been to show that our interactions with our context can affect how our body behaves. I believe few people would entirely disagree with that general point.

I'm also suggesting that most chronic illnesses illustrate the point—that cancer is a context-related behavior change, that arthritis is a context-related behavior change, that diabetes is a context-related behavior change, and so on. I believe significantly more people would disagree with this narrower interpretation.

And I'm suggesting, finally, that we can heal chronic illnesses by reversing the context changes that created them. I believe that *many* more people would disagree with this final point, particularly classical scientists—a category that includes the medical profession.

They disagree almost exclusively on philosophical grounds, however. Their classical training teaches them to believe in molecules at the exclusion of almost everything else. As a consequence, they literally lack the concep-

tual tools to deal with context-dependent behaviors, and
we humans tend not to believe what we're not prepared
to see.

As a consequence (taking cancer as a specific example), the classical scientific perspective says molecules
alone cause cancer and that molecules alone can cure it.
This has become our orthodox medical view, and it has
spawned a multibillion dollar industry that includes
both researchers and practitioners.

A much smaller group of nonmedical practitioners
believes in alternatives ranging from diet to positive
thinking to acupuncture and Chinese healing herbs.
These nonmedical healers say context changes cause
cancer and that context changes can cure it (although
they may not explain what they're doing in precisely
those terms), and for practicing according to these
contextual views, they are called unscientific and worse.

Our question now is what the evidence has to say.

The Mutation Theory

According to medical thinking, cancer cells are off-
spring of normal cells whose genes have been damaged
by "carcinogens"—substances that react chemically with
DNA and produce genetic errors, or "mutations." New
generations of cells inherit these errors, which cause
them to multiply out of control. [1] Since the errors are
irreversible, nothing short of killing the damaged cells
will stop them. The "mutation theory" blames the odd
behavior of cancer cells on an explicitly molecular change.

Yet this mutation theory has never been proven. It is
an assumption—a sort of unquestioned "starting point"
from which medical logic then unfolds. In fact, "the
mechanisms by which chemical carcinogens induce cellular transformation are unknown." [2]

As theories go, the mutation theory isn't a particularly good one. It has "major conceptual problems"[3] and doesn't fit all the facts. As one report put it, "many features of the transformation process are *not* consistent with the somatic mutation theory of cancer."[4]

For example:

- Cancer takes longer to develop than can be accounted for by mutations alone.[5]
- Cancer is a multistep process that unfolds in predictable ways.[6] Random mutations can hardly explain such an orderly and consistent progression.
- Mutations are too rare to account for something so common as cancer.[7]
- Cancer involves genetic transformations that are "quantitatively and qualitatively *unlike* [those] produced by point mutation alone."[8]
- Cases exist where the "mutation" doesn't even occur until *after* the cancer has started.[9]

Although the mutation theory doesn't fit such facts, medicine continues to follow it because it fits philosophically. Once we assume that the behavior of cells depends on molecules alone, it's hard to explain cancer in any other way.

Medical doctors treat cancer by a principle that follows logically from their mutation theory. Since random mutations can't be reversed, a tumor cell is irrevocably damaged and must be destroyed. As a consequence, medical cancer therapies are aggressive and destructive, and the challenge of overcoming cancer is conceptualized as a war.

The Context Principle

The alternative to the mutation theory is the context principle we've been talking about. According to the context principle, cancer cells are ordinary cells behaving normally according to the constraints of their context. If anything is damaged, it's not the cells, but the context that sustains them.

One of the first people to draw scientific attention to the context of cells was a nineteenth-century French physiologist named Claude Bernard. He coined the term *milieu intérieur,* which means "internal environment." Bernard proposed that the main purpose behind the body's complicated physiology was to keep the internal environment constant: "all the vital mechanisms, varied as they are, have only one object: that of preserving constant the conditions of life."[10]

Bernard limited his view of the internal environment to the fluids that bathe the cells, bringing them sustaining elements and carrying off cellular wastes. In general, his was a molecular view. Modern physiologists also emphasize how cells communicate with each other through chemical, electrical, and rhythmic signals,[11] which somewhat extends the view. Contextual science extends the view even further by suggesting that a variable so abstract as *distance from equilibrium* can make a difference. From this contextual point of view, cancer may simply be an entirely natural state that cells spontaneously assume when parameters of their sustaining context get out of adjustment, or fall outside the normal range, in particular harmful ways.

It may be useful at this point to recall the amoebic dysentery example. Scientists identified two strains of amoeba—one virulent, the other benign. The virulent strain would survive on rice powder while the benign strain required a diet of live bacteria. Yet two scientists got the amoebas to shift back and forth from one "strain" to the other by gradually adjusting their diet. Even their genes apparently changed.[12]

The trick to achieving the transformation was to change the context parameter *gradually*. The researchers didn't go directly from bacteria to rice powder, for experience had shown that that would have killed the amoebas. The researchers slowed down the change by inserting a transition diet, one that stood essentially midway between the extremes. This represented a *gradual* adjusting. According to the principles of contextual science, *gradualness* is critical, as this quote from Ilya Prigogine shows:

> When defined in terms of its reversible trans-formations, the *thermodynamic object* may be con-trolled through its [context parameters]: any thermodynamic system whose [context para-meters] are *gradually* changed passes through a series of equilibrium states, and any reversal of the manipulation leads to a return to its initial state.[13]

The emphasis on *"gradually,"* by the way, is Prigogine's.

This gradual adjusting is exactly what the amoeba researchers did. Prigogine applies his statement to what he calls "the thermodynamic object." You may take my word for it that an amoeba qualifies as a "thermodyna-mic object." Paraphrasing Prigogine, then, "An amoeba may be controlled through its context parameters. And when you *gradually* change the context parameters, the amoeba passes through a series of different 'equilibrium states.'" Those equilibrium states are the different states of behavior we've been talking about (like raindrops and snowflakes, virulent amoeba and benign). And further-more, "any reversal of the manipulation returns the amoeba to its initial state." So by *gradually* adjusting noth-ing more than diet, the researchers got benign amoebas to turn virulent, and then by reversing the adjustment, they turned them benign again.

It's interesting in this regard to notice that cancer cells don't have to live on oxygen. They can also live by fermentation.[14] This ability to shift from oxidation to fermentation is by no means unheard of in nature: "Few real organisms are restricted to a single metabolic pattern; most bacteria are sufficiently versatile to live either by fermentation or by respiration . . . *as the occasion demands.*"[15]

Now, imagine that we're back playing with our hypothetical cell-transforming device. We adjust all the levers to produce a vibrant, healthy cell, and then we decide to play around a bit. We adjust the cell's context by *gradually* moving the oxygen lever down. Is it possible that we might see our cell adapt to that gradual change by shifting at some point from oxidation to fermentation, just as bacteria cells do? If so, we will have seen it acquire one of the "abnormal" properties of cancer cells through a simple context change.

These kinds of observations led Albert Szent-Györgyi to propose in 1976 that the problem in cancer is a "lack of oxygen," which has been found to "induce a malignant transformation in tissue cultures. It is easy to believe that a lack of O_2 . . . will eventually take the cells back from the oxidative state to the fermentative state."[16]

Szent-Györgyi went on to say, "Cancer research has greatly been retarded by asking why cancer grows, instead of asking what keeps a normal cell from growing. . . . Cancer was looked upon as a hostile intruder which had to be eliminated. It might be looked upon also as a cell in trouble, which needs help to return to normal."[17]

One reviewer of Albert Szent-Györgyi's work wrote, "the thrust of his research is intriguing; he seeks out the *optimum levels of function in cells* [the balance principle] to determine the *conditions* [the context settings] which should be promoted to help cells maintain accurate replication."[18]

As you can see, Szent-Györgyi's approach is basically what I'm calling contextual healing. Albert Szent-Györgyi was a Nobel Prize-winning biochemist, yet he departed here from the classical scientific model. And his ideas have not been widely accepted.

A Persistent, Nagging Doubt

Szent-Györgyi wasn't the first respected scientist to embrace the context principle. Theodor Schwann, the German physiologist who introduced the cell theory in 1838, proposed the very next year that the basis of life isn't the cell itself, but the "extracellular context"—the context that sustains it—and that cells form within that context "according to definite laws."[19]

The eminent German physician Rudolf Virchow denounced Schwann's view and declared instead that the context "is in definite dependence on the cells."[20] Diseases, he argued, arise from breakdowns in the molecular processes of individual cells. This is the concept of "pathological processes"—the foundation of the mutation theory—and it came about when Virchow explicitly rejected the context principle. His concept of pathological molecular processes has been the medical position ever since.[21]

Yet the context principle has continued to attract scientific advocates, particularly since embryonic cells so obviously depend on their context to unfold in particular ways. Why shouldn't cells follow the same principle after we're born?

In 1935, for example, C. H. Waddington wrote about "individuation fields," his term for the context in which organs form. Then, speaking of cancer, he said, "The fundamental fact about cancerous tissue is that it has escaped from the normal growth-controlling agents of the body. . . . The individuation field, then, is the agent which controls the growth of the different parts in a harmonious way so that a normal individual is formed. . . . These [individuation fields] are the agents from which cancerous growth has escaped."[22] As I mentioned, Waddington's "individuation fields" represent the context that sustains our cells.

As you can see, Szent-Györgyi's context ideas, which he proposed 137 years after Schwann proposed his, represent a subdued but continuing presence in science—a persistent, nagging doubt that says, "perhaps molecules aren't all there is."

Complex, Orderly, and Predictable

In the meantime, evidence for judging between the two perspectives has been accumulating, particularly since 1971 when Congress declared "war" on cancer. Practically all of the research spawned by the "war" has been done by classical molecular scientists following the mutation theory, yet it should give us at least some insight into which of the two perspectives—contextual or molecular—best fits the facts.

Here, for example, are some of the findings:
- Experimenters can easily transform normal cells into tumor cells by altering their context.[23] Sometimes they achieve transformation rates as high as 100 percent.[24]
- They produce the same transformations with many different context changes, including some that don't directly affect the genes—like diet changes,[25] prolonged exposure to heat,[26] rotating experimen-

tal animals slowly on a turntable,[27] and implanting physical barriers that block cell-to-cell communication.[28]

- Small, gradual changes (analogous to the gradual worsening of the amoebic diet) induce tumors far more easily than large, dramatic ones.[29]
- The gene changes involved are very systematic and exceedingly complex.[30]
- These changes occur at a precise moment during cell division, beginning and ending simultaneously at many locations throughout the gene.[31]
- In general, the changes do nothing more than activate dormant genes. These dormant genes often operated before birth, only to be shut down when prebirth development was complete. With these genes reactivated, cancer cells resemble embryonic cells.[32]
- Cells exposed to a degraded context in a dish experience these changes much more rapidly than cells exposed to the same degrading of their natural context within the body.[33]
- Normal cells can become transformed into tumor cells by *nothing more* than the simple fact of being removed from their natural context.[34]

Taken as a whole, these findings suggest that the transformations involved in cancer are very complex, very orderly, and entirely reproducible—just the sort of changes the principles of contextual science would lead us to expect. As Harry Rubin, molecular biologist at the University of California at Berkeley, concludes, "It seems likely . . . that the karyotype [gene pattern] profile of a tumor represents an adaptation of the cells to the particular environment in which they are multiplying and is subject to continuous change."[35]

Declaring Independence

One of the ways this continuous changing shows up in cancer cells is that they "dedifferentiate." This means they lose the unique properties that once let them do particular things and act in particular ways. Since those properties are the ones that let them cooperate with their neighbors to form a particular organ or tissue, they also lose their "tissue-specific characteristics"[36]—the features that identify what functional part of the body they come from.

By analogy, it's as if a Japanese person, removed from Japan, were to lose everything that made him Japanese—his eye structure, his coloring, his language, his mannerisms, and so on—until we could no longer tell what part of the world he came from. Cancer cells have lost all evidence of where they came from. No longer may we discern that they used to be skin cells, or liver cells, or whatever. Their distinguishing characteristics have disappeared.

This is the opposite of what happens to the cells of a developing embryo. Early embryonic cells are essentially all the same. But as the child develops, they gradually differentiate. They acquire tissue-specific characteristics. Eye cells begin to respond to light; muscle cells begin to respond to electrical impulses; skin cells become durable and resilient; and so on. In this sense, cancer seems to be almost a reversing of the context-dependent unfolding that happened before we were born.

The mutation theory assumes this dedifferentiating comes about because the genes get damaged. Yet it may be a simple case of the context no longer sustaining the cell's unique properties. In fact, dedifferentiation relates directly to the concept of distance from equilibrium. A while ago, we called equilibrium "stillness," but it also means "sameness." As a general principle, therefore, systems that move toward equilibrium move toward sameness at the same time, which is to say, they dedifferentiate.

For example, when I was talking about the anti-chiropractic study done on a cadaver, I mentioned that our nerves don't work unless there's a high concentration of potassium inside the cell juxtaposed against a low concentration of potassium on the outside. This juxtaposing of high against low exemplifies the physiological "differences" that exist in the body. Those differences literally keep us alive, and being healthy means keeping them at their proper levels.

Sustaining differences takes internal energy, and if a body drifts toward equilibrium, the differences its internal energy was sustaining start to go away. This is precisely what "dedifferentiation" means, yet we don't have to explain it in molecular terms. Systems naturally dedifferentiate as they drift toward equilibrium, and they redifferentiate as they move back the other way.

So is this why cancer cells dedifferentiate? Do cancer cells emerge spontaneously when the body loses some form of internal energy because we've unwitting maladjusted a few of our context parameters?

To see the general nature of this principle, let's look at Alzheimer's disease. Medical scientists consider Alzheimer's a molecular disorder, so they're looking for a genetic cause, and they're hoping to unravel the molecular mechanisms involved.[37] Yet one of the main things Alzheimer's victims suffer is memory loss, and memory loss is simply another form of dedifferentiation. Could cancer and Alzheimer's disease, which seem so unrelated from the molecular point of view, be due to a common *contextual* principle.[38]

Within this same cluster of changes, cancer cells also

become more hardy. I alluded to this earlier when I pointed out that cancer cells can live without oxygen, which normal cells can't do. They're also better than normal cells at excreting toxic substances,[39] they compete better for nutrients,[40] they experience less DNA degradation,[41] and they repair DNA more efficiently.[42] It's almost as if cancer cells declare their independence from the rest of the body, and experience genetic adaptations that have the specific purpose of enabling them to endure a context that threatens them.

One author summarized the adaptations by saying that they give cancer cells a "growth advantage."[43] They are the very sorts of adaptations that let aphids develop genes for resisting pesticides[44] or that let too-cold fish develop genes for making an "antifreeze protein" as we discussed in an earlier example.[45] The mutation theory says these adaptations are not adaptations at all, but genetic accidents. The context principle says they are entirely *un*accidental—that they are spontaneous, context-dependent expressions of the intelligence within the genes.

Reversing Cancer

And that same intelligence will restore cancer cells to normal when their context is set right. That, at least, is the premise of contextual healing, which a number of studies seem to confirm.

For example, when experimenters transplant cancer cells into a healthy animal, the cells often respond by resuming their normal functions. The only change in such cases is the new context. One researcher claims to have shown "unequivocally" that this return to normal function is identical to the context-driven process that gives cells their individual characteristics in the first place.[46] Harry Rubin summarizes the evidence by saying, "cells that are clearly [cancerous], even to the point of metastasizing under the conditions which initiated the tumor, will lose their malignant character when those initial conditions are removed."[47]

But he qualifies the statement: "if the conditions [that produced the tumor] persist long enough, however, the cells gain the capacity to form tumors in a normal host."[48] In other words, cancer can be more or less easily reversed up to a certain point in its development. Beyond that point, the cells apparently undergo a second transformation that's much more difficult to reverse.[49]

This second, more resistant, transformation may be related to a phenomenon contextual scientists call "the hysteresis effect."[50] The hysteresis effect refers, in essence, to transformations that are harder to reverse than they were to produce in the first place (or easier, depending on your point of view). It's as if ice were to freeze at 32° but not melt until the temperature reached 50°. Applied to cancer, hysteresis could mean that it takes more care to reverse cancer than to avoid it, which seems to be the case. Or put another way, a moderately healthy context may prevent cancer, but only a *very* healthy context will reverse it—in the later stages at least.

Contextual healers claim to achieve these reversals. Medical scientists call their claims "anecdotal" because they're simply stories about what the contextual healers say they have achieved. As we'll see in the next chapter, the heart of classical science is a very precise experimental method that's designed to eliminate all doubts. Contextual healers don't apply that method, so they don't eliminate all doubt as far as classical scientists are concerned.

Occasionally, however, cases come along that are so compelling they can't be denied—cases where patients were clearly dying and now they're clearly well, and no

medical explanation can account for it. Medical literature contains confirmed reports of these surprising
reversals, which medical doctors call "spontaneous remissions."[51] There's no question that cancer patients sometimes get better on their own.

Since spontaneous remissions clearly exist, they are
as much a fact of cancer as the disease itself, and any
good explanation of cancer should be able to account
for them. The mutation theory would have to account
for spontaneous remissions by proposing some molecular event—either a new mutation or a repairing of the
genes—that happens in all the tumor cells at the same
time. The context theory accounts for spontaneous
remissions by proposing that one or more parameters
of the patient's context got adjusted, and the original
transformation reversed itself.

Misdirected Therapies

In light of the context principle, medical cancer treatments seem grossly misdirected. Their purpose is to kill
cancer cells, which they do by flooding their context with
hostile and degrading elements, creating in the process
a host of debilitating side effects in the normal cells.
According to the mutation theory, this debilitating is
necessary because the only other alternative is death.
Cancer cells are damaged and can't be fixed, so treatments
have to be designed to kill them. But the context principle
says such treatments are foolish and dangerous because
cancer cells reflect their context, and treatments that
further degrade the context only make them worse.

Evidence supports this point. For example, patients who
receive chemotherapy treatments commonly experience a
genetic side effect called "gene amplification." This means
that the genes that make the cell cancerous actually become

more numerous. One study linked this side effect of chemotherapy to "shortened survival."[52] Another showed that it "stimulates tumor viability."[53] Award-winning cancer specialist Robert T. Schimke called it "analogous" to cancer itself.[54]

Cancer cells resist chemotherapy the way bacteria resist antibiotics. They keep chemotherapy drugs out of their inner workings. They produce extra amounts of their vital enzymes and even alter those enzymes so chemotherapy drugs won't affect them.[55]

These adaptations have been "correlated with advanced tumour stages and highly aggressive tumour behavior."[56] They have been called "an adverse prognostic indicator,"[57] meaning that they lead to "a very poor short-term prognosis."[58] And they are a direct consequence of chemotherapy, which is itself a context adjustment, but not one that produces health.

Correcting a Misplaced Emphasis

Every seventy seconds another American dies of cancer. That's 1,230 people every day.[59] In 1971, such figures motivated Congress to pass the Conquest of Cancer Act. The idea behind the Act was to "declare war" on cancer—to give medical science a mandate to stop cancer deaths, and the money to do it with.[60] The billions of dollars of research done since then represent a comprehensive test of the explanatory power of medicine's mutation theory of cancer.

Medical cancer researchers have tested more than 800,000 anticancer compounds, and only about forty of them have been approved by the Food and Drug Administration.[61] That's a success rate of .005 percent, and it's just a count of how many tests have resulted in cancer drugs getting through the FDA's approval process, not a measure of cures. The mutation theory's success against cancer itself has been considerably less impressive.

In 1970 (the year before the Act), 17.2 percent of all deaths were from cancer. By 1980 the figure was 20 percent. As we enter the 1990s, some experts predict it may eventually reach 30 percent.[62] Indeed, recent studies "show a steady increase in age-adjusted mortality for all kinds of cancer."[63]

The problem, Harry Rubin says, is medicine's "preoccupation with genetic change in cells as the cause of cancer." He calls this preoccupation "a grossly misplaced emphasis on one part of a multifaceted, dynamic process," a "fascination with trees, which obscures a view of the forest ... [and] ignores the evidence that *genes are only part of the story.*"[64]

So what is the rest of the story? Could it be *contextual?* Could it be the fact that the same system of genes can assume many different states, depending on the context, with one possible state being cancer and another being the state we call "health"?

Perhaps in this "war on cancer" the gentle therapies of contextual healing merit scientific attention as well.

6

How Shall We
Know the Truth?

If contextual healing merits scientific attention, it will
not be through science of the classical sort. Studying
contextual healing with classical science would be like
studying baseball with a book of football rules. Contextual healing and classical science are as different in their
realms as baseball and football are in theirs. They are
different scientific "paradigms," as Thomas Kuhn expresses it.[1] Classical science doesn't deal with matters of
context, while contextual healing disregards molecular
details. Classical science basically ignores distance from
equilibrium, while contextual healing uses it (disguised
as the "balance principle") to explain why the body gets
sick.

Contextual healing and classical science also have
opposite goals. While contextual healing seeks to *express*
nature, classical science seeks to *subdue* it. This alone is
a difference too deep to reconcile.

Distrusting the Intuitive Mind

The idea of *subduing* nature has motivated classical science from the beginning. For example, Francis Bacon, one of the founders of classical science, wrote these words in 1620:

> Knowledge and human power are synonymous, since the ignorance of the cause frustrates the effect; for nature is only subdued by submission.[2]

As to who shall subdue nature, Bacon offers this interesting list:

> the mechanic, the mathematician, the physician, the alchemist, and the magician, but all (as matters now stand) with faint efforts and meagre success.[3]

Bacon believed he knew why these would-be subduers of nature had been having such "meagre" success. They'd been influenced by the Greeks, he said, who "laid their whole stress upon intense meditation, and a continual exercise and perpetual agitation of the mind." In simpler terms, they thought too much. They tried to figure things out, rather than simply observing the operations of nature herself. That emphasis on thinking alone, Bacon said, "has tended more to confirm errors than disclose the truth."[4]

Despite this warning, Bacon's own thinking now led him to a step that would define classical science for centuries to come. He decided to "reject that operation of the mind which follows close upon the senses." In other words, he decided to reject the *intuitive under-*

standing that we spontaneously experience as we use our ordinary senses. In a very fundamental way, Bacon *distrusted* the intuitive mind, arguing that it has "little effect, since the understanding, undirected and unassisted, is unequal to and unfit for the task of vanquishing the obscurity of things."[5]

What do you do, then, if you distrust the intuitive mind? "Our only remaining hope," Bacon said, "is to begin the whole labor of the mind again; not leaving it to itself but directing it perpetually from the very start, and attaining our end as it were by mechanical aid."[6] The key to that sentence is the phrase, "not leaving it to itself." Science must rely on something *beyond* the mind—on some "mechanical aid":

> While we falsely admire and extol the powers of the human mind, we do not search for its real helps. . . . Our present sciences are nothing more than peculiar arrangements of matters already discovered, and not *methods for discovery.*[7]

This, then, was Bacon's key: science would be based on methods for discovery. And those methods, Bacon declared, would do two things. First, they would "penetrate the more secret and remote parts of nature." This is the principle called *reductionism*—the idea of reducing things to their simplest parts. Second, Bacon's scientific methods would "abstract both notions and axioms."[8] This is the principle of *model building,* through which scientists organize the simple parts they define into abstract mathematical models. Following Bacon, these two ideas—reductionism and model building—became the founding principles of classical science, and the tools by which nature would be subdued.

Descartes and the Classical Experiment

Modern science arose upon those the founding principles. Its chief architect was the French mathematician
and philosopher René Descartes. Like Bacon, Descartes
began by distrusting unaided thought:

> I have been nourished on letters since my child-
> hood, and since I was given to believe that by
> their means a clear and certain knowledge could
> be obtained of all that is useful in life, I had an
> extreme desire to acquire instruction. But so
> soon as I had achieved the entire course of study
> at the close of which one is usually received into
> the ranks of the learned, I entirely changed my
> opinion. For I found myself embarrassed with
> so many doubts and errors that it seemed to me
> that the effort to instruct myself had no effect
> other than the increasing discovery of my own
> ignorance.[9]

This distressed Descartes to the degree that he decided
to quit formal schooling and learn what he could from
life itself:

> I entirely quitted the study of letters. And resolv-
> ing to seek no other science than that which
> could be found in myself, or at least in the great
> book of the world, I employed the rest of my
> youth in travel, in seeing courts and armies, in
> intercourse with men of diverse temperaments
> and conditions, in collecting varied experien-
> ces, in proving myself in the various predica-
> ments in which I was placed by fortune, and
> under all circumstances bringing my mind to

bear on the things which came before it, so that
I might derive some profit from my experience.[10]

Descartes' efforts to bring his mind to bear on the
experiences that came before it yielded only this: "I
found in them nothing to give me settled convictions."[11]

This, then, was the issue that occupied Descartes'
mind: *how to be sure of things.* And the problem, as he saw
it, was that he could always explain even simple observations in at least two different ways. Until we sort
through all the possible explanations, we don't really
know what's going on.

But how do we sort through explanations? The mind
alone (subject as it is to error) seems far too weak for
the task. We obviously need something else—some tool
to aid the mind. Like Bacon, Descartes wanted a "method
for discovery"—a method for determining which of all
possible explanations is right.

So he devised a method. It consisted of two basic
steps. First, he would consider the possible explanations.
Then (and this was the key) he would "try to find
experiments of such a nature that their result is not the
same if it has to be explained by one of the methods, as
it would be if explained by the other."[12]

In other words, he would arrange a test so precise
that its design would allow only *one* of the explanations
to be correct. This would allow him to eliminate the
other explanations and establish that *single* explanation
as the truth.

The precisely designed test is the *controlled experiment.*
It is the essence of classical science, and Descartes left
no doubt about what he expected to achieve with it: "we
can . . . thus render ourselves the masters and possessors
of nature."[13]

Models that Mimic Nature

The key, then, is the experiment—an artificial situation that simplifies nature and compels her to reveal a particular truth. Setting up a properly controlled experiment takes an enormous amount of *conceptual* work:

> What must be done is to manipulate physical reality, to "stage" it in such a way that it conforms as closely as possible to a *theoretical description.* The phenomenon studied must be prepared and isolated until it approximates some *ideal situation.*[14]

The conceptual work comes in defining the "ideal situation." It's called "ideal" because it's so simple—the mere *essence* of the system being studied. The system itself stands beyond our grasp—a huge number of parts connected in an immense number of possible ways. Scientists must "devise methods for *compressing* the enormous amount of information contained in such a system to an amount that can be handled by the human mind."[15] This "compressing" is what the ideal situation is designed to do.

You'll recall from an earlier chapter that Henri Poincarè wondered if the universe was stable because classical Newtonian mathematics ignored tiny effects like the drag of the tides upon the moon. Classical scientists ignored these tiny effects in order to "compress" nature into a properly simplified "ideal situation." The ideal situation wasn't entirely real, but everyone assumed it was real enough. It captured the *essence* of the system, after all, and that *essence* was presumed to represent the truth.

Classical scientists also idealize by pretending that

nature consists of lines, circles, triangles, squares, and so on. Those simple forms don't exist in nature, yet we "compress" nature into them. They are "ideal forms"—hypothetical shapes that capture the *essence* of natural shapes. We measure natural shapes *as if* they were triangles, circles, and squares. We perform calculations upon our measurements *as if* they were absolute and sure. And while the results we get may not be entirely accurate, they represent the underlying *essence* of nature, which is more enduringly real (the classical argument says) than the infinity of natural forms.

In the same fashion, experimental scientists simplify natural systems to their enduring essence. They reduce their parts to just a few,[16] and they reduce the connections between the parts to a mathematical logic that their finite minds can grasp.[17]

This is the activity called "model building." Its result is an abstract, highly idealized picture of what is presumed to be the *essence* of reality. And scientists, John von Neumann points out, study the model—not reality itself:

> Right at the start we have to make a statement which you are certainly familiar with, but it is necessary to repeat it again and again. It is that science . . . primarily constructs models. A model is a mathematical construction, which, supplemented with some verbal explanation, describes the observed phenomena. Such a mathematical construction is proved if and only if it works.[18]

While nature is complex and cumbersome, models are streamlined and convenient:

> They are miniatures of the world that we can carry around with us, that we can take out at our

leisure and examine, and that we can tinker
with. We can poke them and probe them and
rearrange their parts. In essence, they are pock-
et toys. . . . The scientist can work at his desk,
in the abstract, and apart from the real world.[19]

To set up an experiment, then, the classical scientist
first creates a model and then he constructs a situation
that mimics it.[20] If his model has three variables, his
experimental situation has three variables. If his model
has five variables, his experimental situation has the
same five variables. And most importantly, the scientist
(while claiming to study nature) actually studies his
model—so as not to become confused. This exact ad
simple modeling is what makes the experimental situation "ideal." Everything but the essence has been stripped
away. All variables that might confound the results have
been "eliminated." Experiments that don't precisely
match a simple model are "invalid." They are "uncon-
trolled"—unable to yield conclusive results.

Medicine and the "Double-Blind" Design

As a classical science, medicine follows this experimental method. It creates experimental situations that are as
simple as the model they mimic. Since medicine's model
includes only molecules, medicine's experimental situations include only molecules. Since medicine's model
excludes context parameters, medicine's experimental situations exclude context parameters. Medical experiments
exclude context parameters by *holding them constant*
(theoretically, at least)—to ensure that they can have no
effect.

By analogy, it's as if we decided to give drugs to
raindrops to see how they behave. Since we can also

change how raindrops behave by adjusting the temperature and the wind, we've got to make sure the temperature lever and the wind lever don't get moved up or down during the experiment. That, in essence, is what medical scientists do. They want to see how our cells respond to drugs alone, so as part of the "experimental design," they try to hold our context parameters constant in order to not become confused.

Of course, this "holding constant" is exactly the opposite of what contextual healers do. Contextual healers *adjust* context parameters. They vary them on purpose—sometimes several of them at a time—just to see how the system responds. Medical scientists just as purposely *don't* vary the context parameters, so the system *can't* respond. And at the same time, they administer a *single* experimental variable, which (no surprise) is a molecule. And with the context parameters held constant, they see the undistorted effects of the molecule by itself. And they assume that the results will still be valid after the experiment is over, in real life, when the context parameters are free to vary again.

The context parameter that medical researchers most anxiously hold constant is *the mind*. Their basic experimental plan involves organizing two groups of patients, then giving the drug to only one of them to see if any differences show up. But the group that gets the drug also gets a potential dose of hopefulness, while the group without the drug gets no such thing. This creates a possible difference in their states of mind—a difference that could contaminate the results. So the researchers eliminate the difference by making the two groups *appear* to get the same thing. In truth, one group gets the drug while the other group gets a neutral substance that mimics the appearance of the drug—the "placebo." But only the experimenter knows who's getting what.

The doctors don't know, nor do the patients. This is what gives the technique its name—the "double-blind" research design. The double-blind design comes with a host of other built-in constraints, almost all of them aimed at eliminating context parameters by holding them constant.

The result is a situation that has the virtue of being conceptually simple, but at the cost of being unreal:

> Scientifically, we give up the shifting and elusive mystery of the world, but, in exchange, we gain the standardized and reproducible abstractions from which we can build precise determinate explanations.[21]

The double-blind experiment has become medicine's unwavering standard of proof. Anything that hasn't met it is considered "unproven." Contextual healing principles haven't met the double-blind standard, and they never will. Double-blind experiments are designed for testing the isolated effects of single molecules, with the context parameters held constant. Contextual healers want to find out what the context parameters do—not in an experiment, but in real life, and not just one at a time, but as they operate simultaneously. So they apply a different standard of proof.

The Witness of Personal Experience

Contextual healing's standard of proof is simple experience. If a real-life context adjustment *consistently* produces a particular effect, that's evidence. Of course, it's not very good evidence until we observe it often enough to know that we can reliably reproduce it. This is how we know that lowering temperature below the freezing point reliably turns water into ice. We've proven it through ordinary experience. And we may discover by the same means how context adjustments affect our health.

We may test dietary adjustments, for example, by simply trying them out. We may test the effects of exercise by exercising, or the effects of thinking hopeful thoughts by thinking hopeful thoughts. And so may we test all other context adjustments—by trying them out and noticing what they do to us.

Superficially, this sounds like experimenting, and in some ways it is. But it differs from *classical* experimenting in several important ways.

First of all, we don't manipulate "ideal situations." We don't create an abstract model and then match it with a controlled experimental design. We work within the situations life hands us—complexity and all.

Second, we don't try to explain anything. We hope for nothing more than to discover healthful effects that we can *reliably* reproduce, and if we find them, we count ourselves successful for that alone.[22]

Third, we don't limit ourselves to manipulating just one thing at a time. It takes several simultaneous context adjustments to call forth a snowflake, and it takes several simultaneous context adjustments to call forth health. Basically, we do whatever it takes to get the results we seek.

Fourth, we don't seek *mathematical* results. We don't even try to attach numbers to what we're doing. And when we talk about our results, we use ordinary language and describe them in an anecdotal way—on the premise that concrete words are richer than abstract numbers.

Fifth, we don't try to "master" the body. We try to coax it into assuming its healthiest natural state. Context adjustments aren't commands, they're opportunities, and we're just trying to discover the opportunities that produce the best possible outcomes.

Classically trained scientists generally reject this kind of anecdotal experience. They consider it unreliable because too many things are going on at the same time. Plus, contextual healers describe their results in ordinary language, which may be rich in meaning, but isn't very precise. And contextual healers don't control molecular processes. They adjust context parameters while leaving the molecular processes entirely to themselves. Medical scientists tend to find this contextual approach foreign to their way of thinking, so they generally reject it. In fact, some of them can scarcely say the words "anecdotal experience" without a tone of open contempt. But the anecdotal experience of the contextual healers at least lets them deal with nature as she actually exists, which classical medical scientists (who study abstract experimental models) can't honestly say they do.

Contextual Scientists Reclaim the Intuitive Mind

Throughout the book, we've been drawing parallels between the old-time ideas of the contextual healers and the new ideas of the contextual scientists. We see parallels here as well, but in one regard they're not exact. Contextual scientists do something contextual healers would never conceive of doing. They build abstract mathematical models, just as classical scientists do. But this difference is more apparent than real, because contextual scientists (unlike classical scientists) build models specifically so they can adjust context parameters in order to see what will happen. This interests them because, even in their simplest models, when they adjust context parameters beyond certain points, something startling happens. Their simple models start to show absolutely unpredictable behavior that's often chaotic, bordering on the bizarre, and generally irrational in the classical sense. These *complex behaviors* are the focus of this new science, and the scientists who study them act as if they were contextual healers. They try things out, in other words, just to see what will happen. And they accept as evidence the witness of their own experience.

For example, the rhythmic pulsing of the "Belousov reaction" (the one that blinks like a flashing train signal, only slower) is one of those unpredictable, irrational, and bizarre behaviors. Contextual scientists have analyzed the Belousov reaction with all sorts of mathematical techniques, but when it comes to really *knowing* how it behaves, they rely on what they observe:

> The most convincing evidence [regarding the behavior of the reaction] comes not so much from [analytic techniques like] the aperiodic time series or even from the phase portraits, Poincarè sections, and one-dimensional maps, but from the behavior exhibited as a control parameter . . . is changed.[23]

In other words, they adjust the context parameter and watch what happens.

The following three quotes also show how completely contextual scientists rely on the witness of their own experience:

> [We seek] to discover as much as possible about the behavior of the system for a wide range of parameter values. . . . The emphasis will be on global . . . and intuitive understanding.[24]

> [Complex behavior] is not apparent by looking at conventional dynamics in the conventional way. . . . One must *search* for this order [by varying the context parameters].[25]

> The [context] parameter is now changed and we study whether the system remains stable.[26]

In these early stages of contextual science, contextual researchers generally adjust a single context parameter, which is like adjusting one lever on our snowflake machine. In that sense, they're like the classical scientists, who vary only one experimental variable. Yet on occasion contextual scientists do adjust two or more context parameters at the same time, and when they do, they see "an incredible richness of behavior."[27] That "incredible richness of behavior" takes an incredible richness of language to describe it. The most interesting parts of their reports are anecdotal, and if you *really* want to understand what's going on, you have to witness the experience yourself.

Benoit Mandelbrot, one of the most respected contextual scientists, points out that our mathematical logic and our intuitive observations sometimes don't match. In that case, he says, trust your intuitive observations:

> A formula can relate only to a small aspect of the relationship between model and reality, while the eye has enormous powers of integration and discrimination.[28]

The idea that "the eye has enormous powers of integration" refers to the sort of *discerning of patterns* that we spontaneously experience as we watch dynamic systems behave in real time. Contextual scientists make their living watching dynamic systems behave in real time, and their confidence doesn't come from mathematical proofs (although they develop them), but from the simple fact that they can reproduce contextual effects time after time after time.

Breaking the Tyranny of Lines, Planes, and Solids

Contextual science also rejects the very foundation of the classical approach—the idea that we can somehow compress nature's patterns to fit within ideal forms drawn with continuous, unbroken lines. In 1962, Benoit Mandelbrot wrote a paper entitled "How long is the coast of Britain?" The answer, he pointed out, depends on how finely we measure. If we measure foot by foot along the coast, we get a longer measurement than if we measure yard by yard—because a foot-ruler measures irregularities that a yard stick misses. If we measure inch by inch, we get a longer measurement still, and for the same reason. If we could somehow measure the coastline of Britain with calipers that span the width of a subatomic particle, it would essentially be infinite[29]—and so would the perimeter of anything else, including this book. *Lines with fixed lengths don't exist*, nor do any of the other finite shapes we imagine.

Mandelbrot wasn't the first person to notice this. Richard Bentley, who kept the British Royal Library during Newton's day, wrote these words:

> We ought not . . . to believe that the banks of the ocean are really deformed because they have not the form of a regular bulwark; nor that the mountains are out of shape because they are not exact pyramids or cones; nor that the stars are unskillfully placed because they are not all

situated at uniform distance. These are not natural irregularities, but with respect to our fancies only.[30]

"Our fancies," of course, are the ideal forms.

Jean Perrin, a French physicist who won a Nobel Prize in 1926, also saw that ideal forms don't exist and understood that this threatened to undermine classical science. "Although wood may be indefinitely porous," he said, "it is useful to speak of a beam that has been sawed and planed as having a finite area." In other words, if we're building a house and want to lay a beam, we lose nothing by imagining that we've measured it.

But strictly speaking, what we imagine isn't true, because wood *is* "indefinitely porous." Magnified a thousand times, the surface we are presuming to measure would look impossibly rough. And if we go still further, Perrin says, and "attribute to matter the infinitely granular structure that is in the spirit of atomic theory, our power to apply the rigorous mathematical concept of continuity [the idea that unbroken, measurable lines exist] will greatly decrease."[31] In fact, it will cease altogether.

Mandelbrot wasn't content to simply notice these curiosities. He explored them, amplified them, enriched them, and came up with an entirely new geometry that has no ideal forms. Mandelbrot's geometry even talks about *fractional dimensions*. If a line is one-dimensional, a square two-dimensional, and a cube three-dimensional, what is 1.4-dimensional? Or 2.26-dimensional? Mandelbrot conceptualizes such things and calls them "fractals." His fractal geometry "liberates the analysis of natural objects from the tyranny of straight lines, flat planes, and regular solids,"[32] and it creates in the process unimaginably beautiful forms that essentially repeat themselves at *all* successively smaller scales, so that the whole is literally enfolded within every single part. Many of our physiological forms show fractal properties,[33] and fractal geometry has even been used to create entirely realistic, computer-generated background scenes (planet and moon surfaces, for example) for movies like *Return of the Jedi*.[34]

With Mandelbrot's new fractal geometry, two classical scientific assumptions have now been shown to be false: we may *not* capture nature in simple, idealized forms, and we may *not* measure her in any absolute sense.[35] With those assumptions stripped away, and with the bizarre and chaotic behavior that even simple systems show when the context parameters are set just so, the foundation of the classical experimental method has been weakened at least and may have been altogether undermined.

Simplicity and the Slaving Principle

How, then, do we cope with the *complexity* that the classical experimental method was designed to address? In their details, natural systems are, in fact, impossibly complex. They consist of countless tiny parts interconnected in countless intricate ways. How will we come to grips with such complexity? Where will we find the simplicity we seek? According to the principles of contextual science, the simplicity comes from the context parameters.

I experienced this contextual simplicity when I played string bass in a dance band. As one of several individual players, I was independent and free to do as I wished. Yet within the context of the band, I integrated with the other players, and they integrated with me. What could have been chaos ended up simplicity.

To achieve this integrating, we operated within a

rhythmic hierarchy with the slow beats at the top setting a basic pace and the faster beats at the bottom accommodating themselves within it. For example, imagine our drummer marking the pace by thumping his bass drum with a whole-note beat (once a measure, in other words). The pianist chords half notes (two beats a measure), while I pluck my string bass in a quarter-note beat. Graphically, we might represent our relationship like this:

Bass drum: 1........................ 1........................ etc.
Piano: ½........ ½........ ½........ ½........ etc.
String bass: ¼..¼.. ¼..¼.. ¼ .¼.. ¼ . ¼..etc.

As you can see, bass drum, piano, and string bass represent three rhythmic levels, with each downward step doubling the pace of the level above. We could continue the principle indefinitely—trumpets playing eighth notes, flutes playing sixteenth notes, and so on— with all of the faster rhythms driven by the bass drum's basic whole-note beat. It never happens this regularly, of course, because the instruments shift between rhythmic levels and syncopate the beats here and there. But you can see the principle.

The body's many levels of natural rhythm integrate in this same fashion, it appears, with the slower rhythms setting the pace for faster ones. And the master rhythm— the one that paces them all—is the sun. People who spend days underground soon find their twenty-four-hour cycle lengthening to twenty-five hours or so.[36] When they again experience the sun, they resynchronize. By the same principle, jet lag puts us out of sync, while recovering from jet lag locks us in sync again.[37]

Organs have rhythms, as do the cells and molecules within them. So do atoms and subatomic particles, with the rhythms becoming faster with each downward step. And all of these rhythms interlock to one degree or another, so that, in a very real sense, our subatomic particles accommodate their ever-so-hurried marching to the majestic pace of the sun.

This is called the "slaving principle." In general, it refers to the fact that when systems exist far from equilibrium, *the contextual forces gain power to dominate the molecular forces* This is because the contextual forces operate at long range while the molecular forces operate only at a very short range—as a sort of molecular "glue."

Imagine a beauty-products commercial in which the model's hair is swept back by the wind into an elegant and graceful curve. The wind represents a long-range ordering force. The short-range molecular forces create the chemical structure of the individual hairs and contribute to the overall pattern, but the *presence* of the pattern is called forth and sustained by the wind, and if the wind dies, the pattern dies as well. A long-range contextual force orders and aligns the short-range molecular forces, and subordinates the parts to the energy pattern of the whole.

This too is the slaving principle. In one or the other of its expressions, the slaving principle is the means by which context parameters exert their effects. Context parameters, to repeat, represent *long-range dynamic forces* that "slave" the short-range molecular forces so that the parts of the system behave freely in a sense, yet only within certain constraints.

As you can see, the slaving principle simplifies complex systems considerably. It gives them an overall order—a pattern that they express as a whole. Imagine a band with a million players. In scientific terms, they represent a million "degrees of freedom," because they're all free to do what they want. But when they lock into the rhythm of the bass drum, those million degrees of rhythmic freedom collapse into one. What was complex instantly becomes simple because the driving rhythm imposes a long-range contextual constraint. All context parameters operate by some expression or other of this same slaving principle.[38]

And this is why we see *global patterns* in systems made from countless independent parts. The parts aren't really independent. They're "slaved"—driven by the long-range dynamic forces of the context parameters. The global pattern comes into existence as a snowflake comes into existence—as a spontaneous consequence of the *interaction* between the long-range forces of the context and the short-range forces of the molecules themselves. As we adjust the context parameters, we adjust the long-range forces. And as we adjust the long-range forces, we adjust the global pattern as well. Discovering the body's natural context parameters and exploring the patterns that they produce is what contextual healing is all about.

Gifts of the Intuitive Mind

It's also what contextual science is all about. And to discern the global patterns, contextual scientists rely on their "intuitive understanding."[39] They study the patterns with nothing more than the eye, to which they attribute, in Mandelbrot's words, "enormous powers of integration and discrimination."[40] Being guided by those enormous powers of integration and discrimination, they trust that they will not be deceived—provided their sample of experiences grows large enough.[41]

And by trusting the intuitive mind, they contradict the assumption that classical science began with. Francis Bacon *dis*trusted the intuitive mind, or as he called it, "that operation of the mind which follows close upon the senses."[42] We must "begin the whole labor of the mind again" he said, "*not leaving it to itself* but directing it perpetually from the very start, and attaining our end as it were by mechanical aid."[43] So generations of classical scientists have compressed nature into abstract, idealized models, claiming to have captured her essence, yet missing entirely the irrational, unpredictable, and even bizarre behavior—not to mention the stunningly *beautiful* behavior—that context parameters call forth.

When G. M. Stratton walked around wearing prism goggles and saw his upside-down world turn itself right side up, he witnessed his intuitive mind at work. When those blind people turned a pattern of pressure on their back into a correctly placed "visual" image, they witnessed a gift of their intuitive minds as well. And when those experimental subjects poked their pointers around in those three model rooms, their intuitive minds revealed to them the presence of odd-shaped angles and walls—a truth that their rational minds had been entirely unable to grasp.

In the chapter on the mind, I talked about how these gifts of the intuitive mind take place within us only when we truly and completely *couple* with our context. That true and complete coupling involves all of our senses in an exploratory venture that exposes us *directly* to the complexity we wish to understand. This direct multisensory coupling is what ordinary experience is all about.

To conduct a classical experiment, we do just the opposite. First we create an idealized model. And then we couple with the *model*, but we do *not* couple with reality itself. And for our sense perceptions we substitute *numbers*—on the premise that our senses (the ones that turned G. M. Stratton's upside-down world around) can be too easily deceived.[44] Idealized experiments *un*-couple us from our natural context.

Alexander Koyre says the advent of classical science

split our world in two: "[It] did this by substituting for our world of quality and sense perception, the world in which we live, and love, and die, another world—the world of quantity, of reified geometry."[45]

Contextual healing seeks to discover the body's natural context parameters and to explore the full range of their effects as they operate in real life. It's an old-fashioned idea, yet it seems again to parallel the principles of contextual science.

Classical scientists generally condemn the contextual healers because they offer no explanatory models and they offer no experimental proof. All they offer is the witness of their ordinary experience and the gifts of their intuitive minds. Are these truly not enough?

7

Contextual Healing's Challenge to Medicine

I've been drawing parallels between the old-fashioned ideas of the contextual healers and the newly discovered principles of contextual science. The parallels aren't absolute, but they are strong enough to challenge the medically oriented critics who often dismiss contextual healing as unscientific and even impossible.

The parallels also weaken medicine's claim to some absolute scientific authority in matters of health. Ilya Prigogine showed that classical chemistry doesn't apply to far-from-equilibrium systems. The human body is a far-from-equilibrium system. Doesn't that suggest that classical chemistry doesn't apply to the human body, at least not as directly and reliably as we've always assumed? What, then, may we say of medicine itself, which claims classical chemistry as its base? How well does classical medicine apply to far-from-equilibrium systems like us?

At the very least, contextual science challenges medical doctors to consider the possibility that their science may be incomplete. If the science of medicine is incomplete, the *practice* of medicine may be incomplete as well. And if the practice of medicine is incomplete, we could be spending billions of dollars for treatments and practices that are, in some measure, scientifically flawed. If this is true, we should be seeing evidence of it—evidence that medicine, in some fashion, isn't working as it should. Let's see what the evidence suggests.

The Compensating Effects of Negative Feedback

In the chapter on cancer, I mentioned a side effect of chemotherapy called "gene amplification." Gene amplification means, in essence, that certain genes in the cell multiply, or grow more numerous. Since genes make enzymes, gene amplification means that cancer cells respond to chemotherapy by making at least one important enzyme in greater quantities than before.[1]

The enzyme that they make in greater quantities is the one the chemotherapy drug blocks. In other words, what the drug is supposed to get rid of, the cell makes in larger amounts—as if it were *compensating* for the drug. This compensating is known as *drug resistance*, and it has the effect of making the cancer worse.[2]

In 1985, a Stanford cancer specialist named Robert T. Schimke won the Alfred P. Sloan Jr. Prize for his research on gene amplification. When a reporter asked Dr. Schimke why cancer cells amplify drug-resisting genes, he said, "I basically have no answer."[3]

Perhaps Dr. Schimke has no answer because he's been trained in molecular science and the answer is contextual. Contextual principles not only explain the resistance; they predict that it will occur.

We can see why by looking again at the Belousov reaction—the one that pulses alternately yellow and clear. For the Belousov reaction to work, two things must be true: (1) the reaction must be kept far from equilibrium and (2) the reaction must regulate itself. That second requirement—that the reaction must regulate itself—is called *feedback*.

Feedback comes in two basic varieties: positive and negative.[4] *Positive feedback* occurs when a chemical reaction *stimulates* itself—when the "product" of the reaction catalyzes its own making. *Negative feedback* occurs when a chemical reaction *inhibits* itself—when the product of the reaction blocks its own making.

For example, when we get injured, a chemical called thrombin helps us form blood clots. Thrombin itself stimulates, or accelerates, the reaction sequence that makes thrombin. As a consequence, the more thrombin we make, the faster the reaction sequence proceeds. Thrombin allows clots to form around our injuries very quickly because the reaction sequence stimulates itself. This is *positive feedback*.

Another reaction sequence makes insulin. As this sequence proceeds, the amount of insulin builds up, just as in the thrombin example. Unlike thrombin, however, insulin *inhibits* its own making, so that the accumulating insulin eventually shuts the reaction off. This is *negative feedback*, or self-inhibition. It allows the body to make just enough insulin to replace what it uses. More generally, it keeps all of our chemical levels hovering, as needed, around more-or-less constant points.[5]

Negative feedback is also the principle behind the thermostat. A furnace makes heat, which in turn serves to shut the furnace off—self-inhibition again. The same principle, therefore, regulates the heat in our homes and the chemical levels in our bodies.

And this is why our cells resist drugs. Through the principle of negative feedback, drugs that *mimic* body chemicals serve to *shut off* the processes that make them. Drugs that *block* body chemicals serve to *turn on* the processes that make them. What we add to the body gets subtracted; what we subtract from the body gets added back. A precise *compensating* therefore occurs.

Chemotherapy drugs *block* cancer-causing enzymes. The absence of those enzymes *turns on* the processes that make them. The drugs therefore produce an effect directly contrary to the one the therapist had in mind.

In a similar vein, researchers discovered a natural "clot-busting" chemical and began giving it to heart attack patients. The patients got new clots faster than ever.[6] Other researchers thought they could lower blood pressure by blocking the chemical system that makes blood pressure go up. Instead they provoked "vigorous compensatory activation" of the same system, and the high blood pressure now got worse.[7]

Setting the Body's "Thermostats"

This compensating suggests that the problem in such cases is contextual, not molecular. To be precise, for one or more context parameters, the body's *distance from equilibrium* seems to be set too low or too high—either too close to equilibrium or too far away. I suggest this possibility because, as we vary distance from equilibrium, we, in effect, raise and lower the body's internal energy. Could distance from equilibrium therefore be the *adjustable* variable that, like a thermostat, keeps our body processes operating at certain levels rather than others.

For example, imagine again a kitchen sink. Water flows in through the faucet and out through the drain, with the water level holding constant at six inches. In

contextual terms, six inches is the "equilibrium level"—
the level at which the water flowing into the sink exactly
makes up for the water flowing out.

And it is adjustable. If we turn the faucet down, the
water level goes down. If we turn the faucet up, the water
level goes up. We adjust the level, as you can see, by
adjusting the context parameter that governs it.

This is a superficial and inept example because it
shows a simple level of physical equilibrium that's not
governed by chemical feedback processes. But I like it
because it's so graphic and clear. It lets us visualize
something going up and down, and even though it's a
grossly oversimplified picture, the point it illustrates
applies, in general, to chemical equilibrium as well.
Whenever we adjust a context parameter, we adjust the
level at which the processes governed by that parameter
will operate.

Suppose, therefore, that the body's chemical levels
are adjusted in this same general fashion. Suppose they're
governed by *distance from equilibrium*, which functions as
a sort of adjustable thermostat setting. If that's the case,
adjusting our context parameters should reset our chemical levels, not in any direct sense (as if *this* parameter
would always adjust *that* chemical level), but in a general
sense—by affecting the overall outcome of many complicated and interconnected feedback relationships. If our
insulin level is set too low, will certain context adjustments
bring it up again? If the chemicals that govern blood
pressure are set too high, will the proper context adjustments allow us to bring them down?

Medical doctors regularly check chemical levels using
blood tests and urine tests. Yet if our chemical levels
reflect distance from equilibrium as I'm suggesting,
those tests (which seem to be measuring molecules) are
actually measuring a *contextual* variable. This immed-

iately places medical doctors in an awkward position. Their therapies, like their explanatory models, are entirely molecular. Yet some of their most interesting problems may have to do with distance from equilibrium, which is contextual, and contextual problems (those that derive from *long*-range forces) can't be corrected by purely molecular means (which are entirely short range). Not only do molecular therapies miss the point in such cases, they also provoke *resistance*—because they artificially alter our chemical levels while leaving the contextual principle that *establishes* those levels entirely untouched.[8]

When Molecular Explanations Fail

Medicine's incompleteness also places its researchers and theoreticians in an awkward position. Being limited to molecules alone, they find themselves unable to account for certain observations that contextual scientists readily explain.

For example, when molecular biologists discovered endorphins (the body's natural morphine), drug company officials immediately envisioned new nonaddictive pain killers—pain killers that people could take for months and years with no adverse effects. Their scientific advisers assured them endorphins couldn't possibly be addicting. "How could our bodies produce an addicting substance?" they argued. "It's unnatural, contrary to the interests of the organism?"[9]

Perhaps that's logical from the molecular perspective, yet contextual principles predict that endorphins used as drugs will be as addicting as morphine itself. Because of negative feedback, endorphins that we take as drugs can only inhibit our natural endorphin production. They artificially alter our natural endorphin level while leaving the variable that establishes that level entirely untouched.

Endorphins are, in fact, as addicting as morphine. Why didn't the pharmaceutical industry's scientific advisors immediately predict this outcome? Probably because addiction is governed by contextual principles, and they think only in molecular terms. Despite their knowledge of molecular details, they failed a simple predictive test because they didn't take contextual principles into account.

Those same contextual principles explain other odd findings that the medical model doesn't predict. For example:

- Penicillin kills bacteria, yet *low* doses of penicillin actually *stimulate* bacterial growth.[10]
- Radiation damages cells, yet cells exposed to *low* doses of radiation outlive cells that aren't exposed at all.[11]
- Carcinogens cause cancer, yet *low* doses of carcinogens actually produce *less* cancer-prone cells.[12]

These sorts of surprising effects show up so often that they've been given a name—*hormesis*—defined as "the stimulation of growth by low levels of inhibition."[13] We could just as easily speak of "the *inhibition* of growth by low levels of *stimulation*." Hormesis has been observed in bacteria, algae, crabs, clams, oysters, fish, insects, worms, mice, rats, ants, pigs, dogs, and humans.[14]

All such instances represent a systematic *reversing* of what we would logically expect. This reversing was first documented in 1888 and has even had an official scientific name since 1943 when "hormesis" was coined.[15] Yet hardly anyone in the classical scientific community pays attention to it. A 1987 article even carried the title, "What is hormesis and why haven't we heard about it before?"[16]

We haven't heard about it, I would wager, because the classical molecular model can't account for it. And as one author explained, there's "a natural unwillingness . . . to write about a phenomenon that is not understood."[17]

When classical scientists do try to understand hormesis, their explanations naturally tend to be molecular. Among other things, it's been attributed to "the induction of a hitherto unknown chromosomal break repair mechanism,"[18] to "a change in concentration of certain growth controlling agents,"[19] and to "the production of radicals or reaction products that stimulate growth."[20] One expert, after commenting that "it is difficult to visualize what kind of mechanism might be involved," claims the evidence "points to a mechanism operating at the subcellular level."[21]

Contextual principles are much simpler, of course, and they seem to explain hormesis quite well. The reversing comes from negative feedback, and only the *low* doses show it because the high doses are more than the negative feedback can compensate for.

Assuming that this contextual explanation is correct, molecular scientists must again decide what to do with a surprising finding that they can't explain. The solution, one of them suggested, is to ignore it: "there is little reason," he argued "to study hormesis as a discrete phenomenon."[22]

A Mismatch Molecular Research Can't Solve

Yet there are compelling reasons for studying negative feedback effects in general:

> Since the dawn of medicine, it has been noted that many medicinal preparations . . . can at first

> produce a specific pharmacological effect and
> then a completely opposite reaction. . . . The
> term used here is "pharmacological inversion,"
> which describes any reverse of the initial reac-
> tion. . . . The textbooks may refer to this inver-
> sion phenomenon as the "side effect of a drug"
> or as a "paradoxical reaction."[23]

Because these reversings harm patients, medical scientists naturally seek to overcome them. Their means,
however, are almost entirely molecular. A Georgetown
University cancer researcher said, for example, "There's
a widespread feeling among people in the cancer field
that further treatment gains will be a result of a much
more detailed understanding of [cancer] cells and an
understanding of the mechanism by which the cells can
adapt to and resist [chemotherapy]."[24] The goal of these
researchers is to break down the presumed molecular
mechanism of resistance—yet the "mechanism" may not
be molecular at all.

I mentioned earlier the case of a "clot-busting" drug
that ended up causing clots to form faster than ever. The
problem, researchers discovered, is that the body responds
to the drug by producing "markedly elevated" levels of
the *inhibitor* to it. This ends up "tipping the balance in
favor of [clot formation]," which was the original problem. This is a typical negative-feedback reversing, yet the
solution the researchers propose is molecular. They
hope to develop a drug that will "inhibit the inhibitor."[25]

Scientists isolated a particularly potent immune system
chemical called interferon. They hailed it as a "wonder
drug" and predicted it would cure cancer. They were
"shocked," one authority said, when it didn't. Interferon's side effects include seizures, liver damage, and
heart problems.

The problem, interferon researchers decided, was that they didn't know enough about interferon. So they isolated three subvarieties—alpha, beta, and gamma—which they tested separately and in combination. Still the side effects persisted.

Now they've isolated at least sixteen subvarieties of alpha interferon alone, and they're hoping one or a combination of them might work. [26] If not, what's the next step—isolating subvarieties of the subvarieties? And what if *that* doesn't work?

One of the main problems with side effects is that they tend to launch what has come to be known as the "cascade effect." This is where one treatment leads to another, which leads to yet another, and so on—"a process that, once started, proceeds stepwise to its full, seemingly inevitable conclusion."[27] One of the first reports of the cascade effect, published in 1966, describes the case of a fifty-three-year-old man who entered the hospital for simple jaundice and left seventy-six days later—dead. The authors of the report drew the whole progression out in a flowchart that shows one therapy leading to another as the side effects mounted. The last "side-effects box" (the eleventh) contains a single word: *Death*. The jaundice probably could have been left alone.[28]

It is entirely possible that all of these unsettling effects come from trying to fix contextual problems with molecular means—a mismatch that no amount of molecular research will solve.[29]

Therapies that Unwittingly Harm

Yet the molecular research continues at an accelerating pace. Drug companies spend billions of dollars developing new drugs, almost all of them based on the premise that we can direct the body with its own substances—the ones it uses to direct itself.[30] It used to be that the only way to get those substances was to purify them from real bodies, either animal or human. Now drug manufacturers "genetically engineer" bacteria (give them new genes, in other words) so that they make "human" chemicals at low cost. As one enthusiast put it, "the mammalian genome represents the new 'medicine cabinet.' "[31]

Yet virtually all of these drugs face the compensating effects of negative feedback. Perhaps this is why we occasionally read news reports like this one:

> More than half the prescription drugs approved by the Food and Drug Administration (FDA) between 1976 and 1985 caused serious side effects that later caused the drugs to be either relabeled or removed from the market, according to a General Accounting Office (GAO) study released yesterday. . . .
>
> The GAO report found that these side effects were common—from a wide range of drugs for treating almost everything from infertility to heart disease—and fairly serious. They resulted in hospitalization, permanent disability, and even death.
>
> The report also found that . . . drugs approved for children were twice as likely to have serious post-approval risks than other medications.[32]

When researchers followed the medical experience of three thousand children throughout the course of a year, they discovered that more than 10 percent of the children experienced at least one adverse drug reaction.[33] During a three-month period at the Johns Hopkins Hospital—one of our nation's finest—17 percent of the patients experienced an average of 1.5 adverse drug reactions each![34]

The *New England Journal of Medicine* published a study in which 2 percent of patients admitted to a university hospital *died* there from the treatment they received.[35] If that figure applies to other hospitals—and it probably isn't too far off, since we count university hospitals among our best[36]—as many as 700,000 people die each year from medical treatment that was supposed to make them well.

In all such tragic cases, caring physicians substituted their intellect for the molecular intelligence of their patient's genes. There are times when this substituting is necessary and wise. But is it wise in cases where the problem is contextual? And how will physicians who know only molecules discern when such cases exist?

The context parameters that might have healed those patients are like the nutrients, water, air, and sunlight that call forth apples from apple seeds and peaches from peach pits. They sustain the molecular intelligence without directing it. Drugs, in contrast, *overrule* the molecular intelligence without sustaining it. Perhaps we shouldn't be surprised, therefore, that they often fail.

The Uncertain Quality of Research

Medical authorities are naturally concerned about these failures, and they explain them as best they can. According to one American Medical Association official, patients suffer in these ways because medicine is advancing so fast and becoming so complex that it's "outstripping the ability of individual physicians to know it all, to understand it all and to apply it in a consistent fashion."[37] The *practice* of medicine, he seems to be saying, has trouble keeping up with the *science* of medicine.

But the problem seems much deeper than that. When Dr. Robert M. Centor, who represents the American College of Physicians, addressed a congressional committee about this issue, he gave these examples of the sorts of things physicians are confused about:

> What is the best way to treat a sore throat? Should we do a culture? . . . If you have a back pain, how many days should you be at bed rest, for 2 days, or 7 days?[38]

Those are hardly complex issues at the forefront of science. Quite the contrary. The problem, Dr. Centor says, isn't too much information, but too little: "I need to have some data," he told committee members. "I just don't have enough data to make such decisions."[39]

That may seem surprising in light of the fact that medical journals publish thousands of research reports every month. One problem, however, is that they're not very good:

> If one's first impression of the world's clinical literature is that of its fearsome immensity, one's second is likely to be that of its appallingly poor average quality. The two are obviously interconnected; the drug literature is overburdened by a vast volume of superfluous and even dangerous rubbish. . . . No physician, confronted with this literature as a whole from week to week, can be very proud of what his profession is on average producing.[40]

A review of the surgical literature confirmed this point. Most of the studies turned out to be weak. And when the reviewers looked at the connection between the quality of the research and the outcome it produced, they found this intriguing trend: the better the research, the more likely it was to show that the technique being tested *didn't* work.[41]

Some studies are actually fraudulent. The *New England Journal of Medicine* reported the case of a medical researcher named Robert A. Slutsky who was found guilty of "reporting numerous experiments that were never performed, reporting procedures that were incorrect or measurements that were never made, and reporting statistical analyses that were never performed." Dr. Slutsky published 137 articles between 1978 and 1985, nearly half of them either fraudulent or questionable.[42]

In 1986, medical researchers at Harvard University retracted a series of articles in which they claimed to have discovered a substance that stimulates the immune system. Their retraction letter conceded that the substance "does not exist," and that the research data they published "are not reproducible and are incorrect." One of them had "manipulated the data to make it look as if the substance existed."[43]

The head of Stanford University's Mental Health Center resigned in May 1987 after the National Institute of Mental Health questioned his use of grant money and asked for a review of his work. Eventually the university had to correct eleven papers published over a nine-year period, concluding that there had been "a serious departure from acceptable scientific procedure."[44]

In 1988, a federal judge sentenced a prominent drug researcher named Stephen E. Breuning to sixty days in a halfway house for submitting fraudulent research reports on a federal grant. Breuning's fraudulent work had "once been highly valued in shaping treatment policy for mentally retarded children." But the research was "never done," and "the results as described under each of those studies had not been obtained." The University of Pittsburgh gave back the $162,000 used to support the research, and Breuning moved to Michigan where he opened a music store.[45]

Most scientific fraud probably goes undetected. According to the *Washington Post*, "The history of science is pocked by revelations ranging from minor transgressions to outright fabrication of data. Ptolemy misappropriated credit for astronomical observations and Newton wasn't above tidying up his calculations. . . . Because stealthy wrongdoing is hard to detect, the frequency of fraud is unknowable."[46]

Dr. Slutsky's fraud, for example, was detected virtually by chance. A reviewer happened to read two of his articles in quick succession and noticed identical data in the supposedly independent reports. Except for that accidental good fortune, "the papers could have been read independently for years without arousing any suspicion about inaccuracy, carelessness, or fraud."[47]

Science's normal safeguards against fraud are replication (where other scientists try to duplicate the results) and peer review (where independent experts pass judgment on research reports). Occasionally replication works—the fraud at Harvard was caught when other scientists tried to replicate it, for example—but most of the time it doesn't: "the modern biomedical research system is structured to prevent replication, not ensure it. It appears to be impossible to obtain funding for studies that are largely duplicative."[48]

As for peer review, the authors who reviewed the Slutsky case describe how idealistic it is:

In January 1987, a total of 752 articles were
published in twenty-six of the journals in which
Slutsky's articles appeared. Each of those articles, plus the articles that were rejected, required review by two or more qualified persons.[49]

Are there enough qualified reviewers, they ask, particularly when the research involves sophisticated techniques at the forefront of science?

The problem becomes even more acute when the
research is conducted by drug companies, who hope to
produce proprietary, patented products:

> More open to abuse by fraudulent investigators
> are reports of symposia sponsored by phar-
> maceutical or instrumentation companies, since
> such documents are usually not peer reviewed.
> Who selected the point of view in a symposium
> report? Who paid for its publication? Was it the
> subscribers (who are presumably motivated by
> wanting to know the results of the studies) or
> the drug company that wants to sell a drug to
> practitioners.[50]

The result of all this is a system in which "detection
[of fraud] cannot be uniformly reliable. . . . The emphasis on competition and the pressure to produce,
while intended to advance the discovery of truth, may
foster a conflict between personal career goals and the
intellectual motivation of scientists to seek the truth."[51]

Is Medicine "Flying Blind"?

What medicine faces, then, is an avalanche of uncertain and sometimes fraudulent research. As Leon Eisen-

berg concludes in the *American Journal of Medicine,* "doctors have an altogether unwarranted faith in the reliability of clinical methods and tests."[52] Dr. David Eddy, who directs Duke University's Center for Health Policy Research, is even more blunt: "We don't know what we're doing in medicine. . . . We're really flying blind on an awful lot of important problems."[53] Even the government's Office of Technology Assessment says doctors can't claim scientific backing for more than about 20 percent of the things they do.[54]

As a consequence, no genuine standards of medical practice exist. This lack of standards is what Dr. Robert Centor was complaining about when he asked, "What is the best way to treat a sore throat? . . . If you have a back pain, how many days should you be at bed rest, for 2 days, or 7 days?"[55]

Standards of practice should keep all doctors on a common track. Yet that apparently isn't happening:

- Doctors prescribe hemorrhoid injections twenty-six times more often in one city than in another city nearby.[56]
- Children in a particular New England state have their tonsils out seven times more often than children who live in a neighboring state.[57]
- A RAND Corporation study found that up to a third of medical procedures aren't necessary, and that by eliminating unnecessary heart-bypass surgeries alone, we could save patients a billion dollars a year.[58]
- In 1982, Boston's per-patient medicare expenses were almost twice as high as New Haven's, even though the pertinent demographics of the two cities are practically the same.[59]

Why do these inconsistencies exist? What standards of practice are being applied?

Dr. John Wennberg, the Dartmouth physician who first researched these uncertain standards, blames them on "inadequately tested theories of treatment."[60] In other words, doctors often do things they don't have evidence for, and they don't really know what works and what doesn't.

According to Dr. Wennberg, medicine faces an "intellectual crisis."[61] Its therapies now appear much less certain than doctors have been willing to admit. Denying the uncertainty may no longer be possible. As Dr. Frederick Robbins, Dean of Case Western Reserve's medical school, says, "You can cover it up all you want, but it looks bad because it is bad. It is not an appropriate way for a profession to behave."[62]

A Last Remaining Bastion

Over 350 years ago, Francis Bacon noted that the physicians of his day were having "meagre success."[63] Their problem, he suggested, was that they lacked "methods for discovery"—methods that would "penetrate the more remote and secret parts of nature" and "abstract both notions and axioms." Modern medicine is the child of Bacon's suggestion, yet where chronic illnesses are concerned, its success seems scarcely less "meagre" than before.

What if all the problems I've listed here come from the simple fact that classical science ignores context variables. This ignoring is supposed to *isolate* systems so scientists can study them uncontaminated by any confounding influences. Yet those "confounding influences," we see now, are as essential as the molecular system itself, and may even be the key to healing.

Medicine is one of classical science's last remaining bastions. It is very likely incomplete, and if it is incomplete, it cannot completely succeed—a clear possibility that dramatically affects us all.

Medicine's challenge, therefore, is to consider its fundamental incompleteness and acknowledge the possibility that molecular therapies alone may not solve the challenges it faces. Such honesty won't be easy because it will very likely mean that medical doctors must now share the field of healing with contextual healers, whom they have long considered frauds. Difficult as that may be, however, it may be the only acceptable choice.

8

Contextual Healing's Challenge to Our Lawmakers

If medical doctors become willing to acknowledge the incompleteness of their medical model and share their market with the contextual healers, it will be a strong step toward the health-care smorgasbord I envisioned in the first chapter. An even stronger step—which we must take whether medical doctors acknowledge their incompleteness or not—is revising our medically oriented health-care laws. In many states, parents can lose custody of their children for refusing medical treatments they don't want. Health-product manufacturers can be prosecuted for promoting contextual therapies that medical science doesn't approve. And therapists who use nonmedical treatments can be sent to jail. Such restrictions are based on the mistaken premise that medicine is the only valid healing principle.

Because of that promedical premise, our laws put

contextual healers in the unworkable position of being required to prove their validity by the double-blind standards of classical medicine. The normal judicial standard of *personal witness* (which is also the standard of contextual science) has been supplanted by the "evidence" of *scientific consensus*. Our laws also assume that ordinary citizens aren't capable of making wise choices in matters related to health—that the only truth in such matters is scientific truth. These are precisely the premises of classical science—the premises of Francis Bacon and René Descartes—yet they have been written into our laws.

The error in this is that scientific truth is not etched in stone, whereas our laws tend to become so. Scientific truth, as historian Lynn White so eloquently put it, is "not a citadel of certainty to be defended against error; it is a shady spot where one eats lunch before tramping on."[1] So science tramps on, while our laws stay in the shady spots of yesterday's lunch—unless we are wise enough to change them.

When Our Children Become Ill

Should we not change our laws, for example, to preserve for parents the right to care for their children as they see fit? We might consider this right fundamental—perhaps too self-evident to be the subject of debate. As our laws presently stand, however, parents generally *don't* have a firm legal right to contradict medical authorities who may disagree with them. They are denied this right on scientific grounds.

In Kentucky, for example, an Amish man named Danny Mast went to jail for refusing to turn his cancer-stricken son, Amos, over to medical authorities. Mr. Mast preferred to treat Amos with herbs, while the

medical authorities insisted on chemotherapy. The judge
ruled in favor of the medical authorities and ordered
Mast to relinquish custody of his boy. When Mast instead hid Amos with relatives, the judge jailed him, and
released him four days later only after he agreed to
medical treatment. I spoke with Mast's attorney, James
Gregory, with the local reporter who covered the case,
and with the clerk of the judge who jailed Mast. All
agreed that the only "neglect" Mast committed was to
disagree with the doctor's recommendation. Roughly
five weeks after the hearing, Amos Mast died.[2]

Based on the information I present in this book, I'm
persuaded that cancer is contextual, and that chemotherapy creates a significant risk of making cancer worse.
As a consequence, if my child had cancer, I would treat
him contextually and would probably (among other
things) use herbs.[3] Being curious how I would fare in
such a case, I looked up Utah's child neglect law. A
section of it says this: " 'Neglected child' includes: . . .
(c) a child whose parent, guardian, or custodian fails or
refuses to provide proper or necessary . . . medical care
. . . or any other care necessary for his health."[4] Then I
called the juvenile court and asked the clerk if that
section of the code was ever used to force parents to
subject their children to medical treatment they don't
want. She said, "It happens all the time."

According to a report on nonmedical cancer treatments prepared for the federal government's Office of
Technology Assessment (OTA), a review of two similar
child-custody cases showed that "how the courts weighed
the *evidence of effectiveness* of the available treatments
seems to have played more of a role in their decisions
than the concern for a right to family privacy."[5]

In other words, scientific judgment carried more
weight than the judgment of the parents, even when it

concerned a child the parents alone had borne and raised.

The Limiting Effects of Licensing Laws

If I had a child with cancer, I would probably consult an expert on Chinese herbs.[6] I've been particularly impressed by a report published in the journal *Cancer* that describes Chinese herb research conducted at the University of Texas. According to the report, one Chinese herb restored the normal immune response in cancer cells 90 percent of the time.[7]

One of the senior researchers on that project was a Chinese herb expert from Beijing, China—a Dr. Yan Sun—who collaborated with the University of Texas scientists. Imagining that I might seek the counsel of someone like Dr. Sun, I called the director of our state's Division of Occupational and Professional Licensing to see how that might be arranged.[8]

I told the director about the University of Texas study and asked something like this: One of the researchers on that project was an herb expert from China—apparently one of the best. He's not licensed to practice medicine in Utah, however. Suppose one of my children got cancer. Could I invite that Chinese herb expert into my home to treat my child with his herbs?

The director answered, in essence, that if the Chinese herb expert tried to treat my child with herbs—even at my request and in my own home—he would be guilty of a felony crime.

I asked the director under what circumstances the Chinese herb expert could legally treat my child or how I might otherwise gain the right to use the herbs. He told me this: If I could find a licensed physician interested in using the herbs, that physician could file a plan with the hospital where he worked and ask the institutional review board to review it. Only if the board approved the plan, and only if the physician filed all the proper informed-consent papers, could he proceed. The physician, then, not the Chinese herb expert, would be required to do the treating, and he would have to prove that he was operating within the standards and ethics of medical science. Otherwise he would risk losing his license. Few physicians would try it, the director said, because "I think they're afraid."

All states have laws that define both who has a right to practice medicine[9] and how they can lose that right. All states also set up medical review boards for disciplining doctors, and in all states, doctors can lose their licenses for using therapies that the review boards don't approve.[10] According to the OTA report I mentioned earlier, these laws "might make it difficult for some practitioners to comfortably offer patients care they believe is beneficial to them if they believe their ability to practice medicine might be jeopardized."[11]

When the director said, "I think they're afraid," this is what he meant.

Natural Products and the FDA

I'm also interested in certain plant extracts made in Europe. They're widely used over there and are available here as well, but the advertising literature we receive here in America essentially says nothing about them. So I called one of the European plant-extract manufacturers (a major pharmaceutical company with many millions of dollars in annual sales) and asked (referring to a specific product), "Why don't you tell American consumers what this product is supposed to do for them?"

The problem, the company's spokesperson told me,[12] is that the U.S. Food and Drug Administration prohibits them from describing the product's value, despite the fact (which I confirmed) that European scientific journals have published many dozens of research reports on it. When the company first decided to enter the U.S. market, they hoped to get the extract approved and felt (given the size of the market) that they would do whatever it took. But when they spoke with consultants who guide companies through the FDA's approval process, they were told that they would be foolish even to try. The FDA, the consultants said, would probably require that they isolate all of the extract's active ingredients and then go through the approval process separately for each one of them. At tens of millions of dollars per active ingredients (and without being able to protect their investment with a useful patent, since plants aren't patentable[13]) it would hardly be worth the effort.

I wanted to check two of his statements: (1) the idea that the approval process costs tens of millions of dollars, which could be unrecoverable without a patent, and (2) the idea that manufacturers of plant products might be required to isolate active ingredients and get them individually approved. I instantly saw that if these statements are true, natural-product manufacturers face genuine obstacles—virtually insurmountable obstacles—in getting their products approved by the FDA.

To check his statement about costs, I called the Pharmaceutical Manufacturers Association and asked, "How much does it cost to get a drug approved by the FDA?" They didn't have a separate figure for FDA-related costs, but they set the average cost of getting an *already developed* drug to market at $125 million. They confirmed the figure by sending me a report entitled "The Cost of Developing a New Drug," by Steven N. Wiggins, Rex B.

Grey Professor of Economics at Texas A&M University.[14]

I called the FDA and asked the same question: "How much does it cost, on the average, to get a new drug approved?"

The FDA doesn't keep cost figures, their spokesperson told me,[15] but when I mentioned the $125 million figure I got from the Pharmaceutical Manufacturers Association, he said he doubted very much that that amount could be attributed to the FDA's requirements. The figure covers research a manufacturer would have to do in any case, he said, and most likely includes overhead expenses that are simply normal costs of doing business.[16] With or without FDA approval, he was suggesting, the costs for developing a new drug would be more or less the same.

Perhaps. But Dr. Wiggins' report suggests that this official view may be a bit optimistic. Our current drug-approval requirements come from the 1962 Kefauver-Harris amendments. Before the amendments, forty-seven drugs were being approved each year, at an average cost for research of $3.7 million. When the amendments were adopted, the number of new drugs immediately dropped to thirteen per year, while research cost per drug rose to $40.4 million—in 1960s dollars![17] By those standards, the current $125 million figure sounds plausible indeed—and so does the idea that FDA's medically oriented approval requirements account for much, if not most, of it.

To answer my second question, I spoke to one of the FDA's approval specialists.[18] "Are manufacturers of plant products required by law," I asked, "to isolate a plant's active ingredients and get each one of them approved separately?"

"No," she said. "All a manufacturer has to do is

submit a protocol, or a research plan, get it approved, and follow it. The protocol must follow accepted scientific standards, of course, but beyond that, there are no specific requirements."

I said, "I assume the scientific standards you apply are the ones that govern medical research?"

She said, "That's correct."

I asked, "Within those standards, is there any reason why manufacturers of plant or plant extract products would have to isolate individual chemicals and submit them separately?"

She said, "They would have to show they could manufacture a consistent product. And to do that, they might have to know what's in the plant that produces the effect and then prove they can control its manufacture. That's pretty hard to do if the effect comes from some mixture of things you haven't identified. But if you can create a protocol that lets you do all that with a complex natural substance, nothing in our regulations prevents it. Most manufacturers don't deal with plants because natural products aren't consistent, and they're not a very reliable source. Plant supplies vary from year to year, so prices tend to go up and down. Since synthesizing chemicals gives manufacturers so much control, few of them look to plant sources. We hardly ever get requests to approve natural substances."

I'm quoting from my rough notes of the conversation, so the words aren't exact, but I believe I've faithfully represented the essence of what she said.

Both the tone and substance of her words suggested that anything is possible. Yet she also acknowledged that a review board judges proposals by the strict standards of medical science. Anything not meeting those standards is disallowed, and medical standards emphatically prefer isolated substances over whole plants.

From what I learned, the idea that European manufacturers of plant-based products may be foolish to seek FDA approval seems reasonable, although no regulations explicitly prohibit them from doing so. And I'm not surprised that the FDA hardly ever gets requests to approve natural substances.

A *USA Today* reporter asked then-deputy FDA commissioner John Norris how readers could tell which cancer remedies are legitimate and which ones aren't. A legitimate product, Norris said, has been "approved by the FDA or approved as an investigational new drug." Otherwise, he said, "it is a bogus remedy and they should seek a second opinion before they allow themselves potentially to be killed or maimed."

According to Norris, the vast majority of manufacturers of nonapproved products are "gangsters motivated by greed and willing to exploit people who are desperately ill."[19] Yet the cost of getting the FDA to approve natural, plant-based health products may be more than anyone can bear.

Redefining Fraud

Just as no regulation *explicitly* prevents natural-product manufacturers from gaining FDA approval, no regulation *explicitly* prevents us from choosing the healing remedies we prefer. Yet we are *practically* prevented from choosing nonmedical remedies when parents who disagree with a medical doctor may lose their children, when contextual healers may commit felony crimes by treating us in our homes, and when manufacturers not only can't tell us what their products do, but may even become *gangsters*, simply because they haven't gone through an approval process that may, in fact, be impossible.[20]

Because of this, many health consumers (I include myself among them) argue that our present health-care laws give medicine a practical monopoly and deny us a Constitutionally guaranteed freedom of choice. According to this "freedom of choice" argument, the U.S. Constitution guarantees to all citizens a fundamental right to privacy, and laws whose practical effect is to restrict health care to a *particular* healing philosophy—whether medicine or any other—necessarily infringe upon that right and restrain our freedoms in constitutionally prohibited ways.

Those who favor our current health-care laws justify their position by arguing that the Constitution delegates to federal and state governments a fundamental obligation to protect the health and safety of their citizens. According to this "consumer protection" argument, requiring that products and therapies be scientifically proven safe and effective is a reasonable and rational way to carry out that Constitutional responsibility.

Few debates in contemporary society (the abortion debate being a notable exception) divide Americans more heatedly and bitterly than this one.

I suggest, however, that the "consumer protection" argument fails by mistakenly equating science and orthodox medicine. As I've tried to show in this book, medicine descends from classical science, and a new scientific perspective now exists that parallels the "vitalism" of the old-time healers in remarkable ways. Contextual science now claims a scientific position that is at least as strong as the classical position and even surpasses it for studying health. As Ilya Prigogine says, "The deterministic laws of physics [the one's medicine is based on], which were at one point the only acceptable laws, today seem like gross simplifications, nearly a caricature."[21] Do we truly protect the public health by enshrining those "gross simplifications" within our laws?

As Prigogine points out, the classical scientific laws "were at one point the only acceptable laws." This was the case in 1906, when the first federal Food and Drug Act was passed. That was only four years before the last eminent vitalist died in 1910 and science was "released" from vitalism's "bonds."[22] The spirit of those times declared that all "vitalists" were quacks and frauds, and that same spirit persists today.

By accepting this historical accident as if it were truth, our lawmakers have drawn the legal battle line in the wrong place. Practically speaking, our current health laws define fraud *philosophically*—as if medicine were entirely legitimate and contextual healing were entirely fraudulent. Figure 2 represents this *philosophic* definition of fraud:

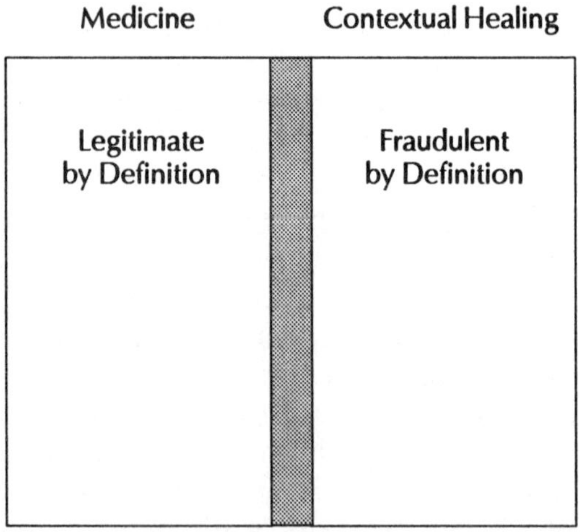

Medicine	Contextual Healing
Legitimate by Definition	Fraudulent by Definition

Figure 2. Practically speaking, our medically oriented health-care laws define fraud as a *philosophic* act.

The truth, of course, is that fraud exists in both medicine and contextual healing. And so do legitimate products and practices. Shouldn't we write our laws so that they prevent the *criminal* act of fraud, not the philosophic act of disagreeing with the established medical authorities? Figure 3 represents this *criminal* definition of fraud:

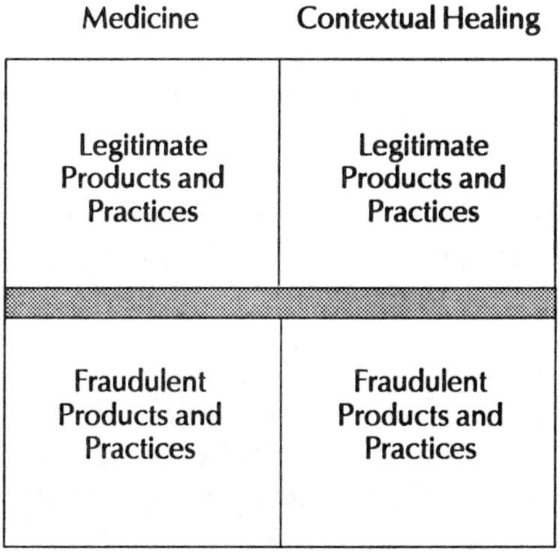

Medicine	Contextual Healing
Legitimate Products and Practices	Legitimate Products and Practices
Fraudulent Products and Practices	Fraudulent Products and Practices

Figure 3. Wouldn't we be wiser to define health fraud in purely *criminal* terms?

Of course, if we were to define fraud in criminal terms, the task of rooting out the criminals might become a bit more challenging because we wouldn't be able to ask the medical authorities anymore. We would probably have to guarantee people a trial before a jury of their peers, presume that they are innocent until proven guilty, and even rely on the evidence of personal testimony. As our health laws presently stand, these normal safeguards don't always apply.

Assuming the Need to Protect

Having said all this, I believe there is a still more fundamental issue. It has to do with the basic assumptions underlying the "consumer protection" point of view—the point of view that justifies our current medically oriented health-care laws. As stated in the OTA report that I've mentioned twice now:

> The "consumer protection" point of view is supported by the contention that the average consumer cannot be expected to make informed choices in a complex scientific field.[23]

To support that contention, the report cites "an early court case under the Food and Drugs Act of 1906" in which the judge said:

> This law was not passed to protect experts especially, not to protect scientific men who know the meaning and value of drugs, but for the purpose of protecting ordinary citizens.[24]

The distinction here between "ordinary citizens" and "scientific men who know" presupposes that "ordinary citizens" do *not* know.

The OTA report also cites this statement made by Supreme Court Justice Felix Frankfurter as he interpreted the 1938 Food, Drug, and Cosmetic Act:

> The purposes of this legislation . . . touch phases of the lives and health of people which, in the circumstances of modern industrialism, are largely *beyond self-protection.*[25]

Finally, the president of the National Council Against Health Fraud, one of the most outspoken supporters of the current system of health-care laws, wrote this:

> Should we license and give medicare dollars to alchemists, witches, herbalists, health food therapists, faith healers, etc., on the assumption that the consumer will be wise enough to choose the proper kind of care, and within sufficient time to protect his life and health?[26]

The first assumption, then, is that consumers are not wise enough to protect themselves.

The second assumption is that molecular medicine, representing the classical scientific community, sets for government an absolute standard of truth in matters pertaining to health. I refer again to the OTA report:

> A formal set of procedures, consistent with the 'scientific method' . . . has been incorporated into the processes and standards of evidence required by the Federal Government for the approval of new drugs and medical devices.[27]

This 1974 ruling defined the "standards of evidence":

> The purpose of normal inquiry [into the safety and effectiveness of drugs] is not to determine safety and effectiveness at all, but to ascertain the drug's *general reputation in the scientific community.*[28]

The "scientific community" is medical, of course, and the "evidence" it offers is this vague notion of a therapy's "general reputation."

We see the same vague notion in the Nutritional Labeling and Education Act of 1990, which allows nutritional claims on food products only if

> the Secretary [of Health and Human Services] determines, based on the totality of publicly available scientific evidence . . . that there is significant scientific agreement, among experts qualified by scientific training and experience to evaluate such claims.[29]

What is "significant agreement"? And are purely molecular scientists "qualified by scientific training and experience" to evaluate contextual claims?

Reaffirming the Source of Wisdom

Our present health-care laws assume, then, that ordinary citizens are not wise enough to choose for themselves, and that classical scientific opinion sets for government a legal standard of truth. I find these assumptions significant because they are *not* the assumptions underlying the Constitution. The Constitution assumes that the power to govern resides within ordinary citizens— a power that we delegate to those who govern us—and that those who govern us are not our rulers, not even our partners, but our servants, doing as we, the people, direct.[30]

There's not even so much as a hint in these assumptions that we ordinary people aren't wise enough to choose for ourselves. Just the opposite, in fact. Early Supreme Court decisions even went so far as to declare the source of our wisdom. It resides, an 1823 decision states, in "those principles of abstract justice, which the Creator of all things has impressed on the mind of his creature man."[31] An 1840 decision points to "the source of eternal justice as it comes from intelligence and truth."[32] This, then, is why the Constitution gives to ordinary citizens the power to govern: the "Creator of all things" has endowed us with a capacity to discern the truth. This, clearly, was a capacity that our delegated governors were expected to honor and to protect.

This assumption was undermined, however, by the philosophic victory of classical science. By 1887, with that victory by now clearly in hand, a U.S. Supreme Court decision declared a new source of wisdom:

> Out of the domain of the exact sciences and actual observation there is no absolute certainty.[33]

And *this* assumption—not the original constitutional assumption—governs our current health-care laws.

Perhaps the new assumption is justified, we might argue, in a field so complex as health. But Thomas Jefferson anticipated that our wisdom might be taxed:

> I know of no safe depository of the ultimate powers of the society but the people themselves; and if we think them not enlightened enough to exercise their control with a wholesome discretion, the remedy is not to take it from them, but to inform their discretion by education.[34]

And wasn't Samuel Butler correct when he said, "The public does not know enough to be expert, yet knows enough to choose between them."[35]

Contextual healing and the new contextual science both assume (1) that we have an innate capacity to discern patterns, (2) that health exists as a particular discernible pattern characterized by a balance between two functional extremes, (3) that we can learn to estab-

lish that balance by adjusting our context parameters, and
(4) that the principles for adjusting our context parameters
represent reproducible and discernible truths. In this regard,
contextual healing and the new contextual science seem
to agree with our founding fathers.

Our present-day lawmakers would be wise to keep
this fact in mind. Because of these new contextual
principles, they can allow us freedom to choose *and still
be scientific*, if being scientific is what they aspire to do.
Furthermore, if they will only stop trying to protect us
from our presumed *ignorance*, they will be sustaining our
nation's founding fathers, who assumed that, except for
clearly limited exceptions that the Constitution explicitly defines, we can—and must—learn to govern ourselves.

By enacting health-care laws that assume we have to
be protected from our ignorance, our lawmakers have
supported instead the founding fathers of classical science,
who, with entirely noble intentions, *wrongly* assumed
that scientists alone—endowed with knowledge that ordinary citizens could not possibly possess—would become the masters and subduers of nature.

If the Creator of all things informs our wisdom as our
founding fathers assumed, and if we may therefore use
that wisdom to direct those who wish to govern us, we
may expect to remain free. If, on the other hand, classical science is the only source of truth, then science alone
can direct those who govern us, and we, along with the
rest of nature, must finally be subdued.

Contextual healing's challenge to our lawmakers is to
decide—and by the Constitution they must decide under
our direction—which of these assumptions will guide
them as they seek to preserve the public health.

9

Contextual Healing's Challenge to Each of Us

If we are to govern ourselves in matters of health, we must understand the basic principles of contextual healing. For most of us (given how we've been indoctrinated in another perspective), that will take a complete overhaul of our thinking. In this chapter, I summarize that overhaul in terms of seven basic postulates. They are:

- Health exists spontaneously in nature when the contextual conditions are right.
- We have a personal stewardship to create the conditions of health for ourselves and for our families.
- To guide us in our personal stewardships, we have been endowed with an innate capacity for discerning beauty and truth.
- By following our innate capacity for discerning beauty and truth, we may gain wisdom, which is the greatest of all gifts.

- In the long run, nothing can substitute for our personal stewardships.
- Governments cannot promote the general welfare by taking over the personal stewardships of their citizens.
- Through the principles of contextual healing our problems may be turned into strengths.

As you can see, the seven postulates are philosophical, not scientific. They refer, for example, to beauty, truth, and wisdom, which classical science doesn't deal with at all. In fact, by the standards of classical science, beauty, truth, and wisdom are useless concepts, because they can't be measured or defined.

But that doesn't mean they don't exist. It just means classical science can't deal with them. I made the seven postulates philosophical on purpose because I wanted to emphasize how much science has changed since scientists began thinking in contextual terms. By shifting scientific attention from parts to patterns, contextual scientists have reintroduced *intuitive* understanding as a scientific tool. And they have seriously shaken (and perhaps undermined altogether) the once-unassailable notion of *rational* understanding, which is classical science's base. (The difference is the one Justice Potter Stewart referred to when he said he couldn't define obscentiy, but he knew it when he saw it.)

And this is part of the overhaul that contextual thinking requires. We must stop focusing on parts and start noticing patterns. We must become willing (in what is essentially an act of faith) to set aside purely rational thinking when our intuitions lead us to a higher, more enchanting view. And we must accept that such things as beauty, truth, and wisdom actually exist and that they can once again become part of our life. This is contextual healing's challenge to us. The seven postulates give shape to that challenge and guide us toward that higher, more enchanting view.

First Postulate: Health exists spontaneously in nature when the contextual conditions are right.

When we talk about "health," we're usually referring to the body or the mind. But in a general sense, the idea of "health" is as broad as life itself. A family is healthy when its members love each other, when they treat each other kindly, and when they do their duties willingly and without complaining. A business is healthy when it sells something wholesome and useful, when its managers and employees work together in an atmosphere of cooperation and respect, and when it makes a profit that is fair and just. A nation is healthy when its government earns the honor of its citizens, when its citizens govern themselves to the degree that they are able, and when its citizens are educated and voice their will, so that government is guided by its citizens rather than the reverse. The body and mind are healthy when they assume the state of balance that we've been considering all along.

According to the principles of contextual healing, each of these states of health is simply one of the many possible states that a system may assume. Whether or not health exists depends on how we've adjusted the context parameters involved. Under certain parameter settings, health spontaneously emerges. Under other parameter settings, it just as spontaneously disappears, replaced by some less healthful state. This is the point of the snowflake example that we've carried as a theme throughout the entire book.

In this sense, health *always* exists, just as snowflakes *always* exist. Even in the heat of a Fourth of July parade, we could call forth snowflakes in an instant if we had access to the context parameters and the wisdom to set them right. In one sense, adjusting the context parameters would bring the snowflakes into existence. But in another sense, it would simply change the *nature* of their existence—from potential to expressed.

This idea can become a source of hope. If I see my child misbehaving, I can say to myself, "His misbehaving is no more 'the truth' than is his goodness. It's just that one is expressed and the other is not. Now, let me see if I can discover some context parameters that I might adjust in order to call his goodness forth." And given time, as long as I don't get frustrated and lose the vision of his goodness, I could learn, I would wager, to at least help call his goodness forth.

By the same token, being chronically ill is no more "the truth" than being chronically well. It's simply a matter of which state happens to be expressed. Given time, and as long as we don't get frustrated and lose the vision of what we seek, we can learn, I would wager, to adjust our context parameters in a way that will make us well.

For most of us, this is probably a new way of looking at things. The old way had us looking at our children and seeing the things we don't like, or looking at our bodies and seeing what annoys us or makes us feel afraid. This contextual way of looking at things takes our vision *beyond* the things we don't like to the entirely *real* potential of whatever beauty we may wish to call forth.

I spoke in an earlier chapter about helplessness, and about how it cuts off the powers of our mind. This new way of seeing is an *antidote* for helplessness. By allowing us to envision the possibility of health, and by giving us principles for calling it forth, the principles of contextual healing can become a source of hope.

One of the contextual scientists I studied is I. I.

Blekhmann. His specialty is synchronization—the principle by which rhythms function as a source of pattern and order. In his book, *Synchronization in Science and Technology*, Blekhmann wrote, "The author is pleased that the teachings of synchronization as described in the book are optimistic. Synchronization phenomena testify to the presence in our environment of strikingly expressed tendencies toward hierarchy and order." This is the kind of hopefulness that contextual healing can inspire.

The first postulate, then, is that health exists *spontaneously* in nature when the contextual conditions are right. All we have to do is to find the context parameters, then adjust them and watch what happens until we call forth the patterns we seek.

Second Postulate: We have a personal stewardship to create the conditions of health for ourselves and for our families.

This postulate is about what some people call "taking responsibility" for our health. I prefer to talk about our stewardships.

I once looked up "stewardship" in a dictionary of word origins. It said "stewardship" comes from the word "sty," meaning pig sty.[1] Although the dictionary didn't elaborate, I would wager that the meaning of stewardship came from the days when a pig sty might have been the greatest wealth a property owner possessed. He would have put his most faithful servant in charge of the sty, no doubt, and given him a charge to take care of it. This most faithful servant would have been the "warden of the sty," or the steward.

But the steward's charge, I like to imagine, involved more than ordinary care. He was to *improve* the pigs, to enhance their value, to give back more than what was originally placed in his care. And he would have fulfilled his stewardship, in large measure, by adjusting the context parameters involved.

We've been given stewardship over our bodies. Our charge is to improve them, to enhance their value. We have similar stewardships over our families, over our businesses, and over anything else that comes under our care. To be given a stewardship means to be given access to the context parameters that enhance value. Our job, whatever the nature of the stewardship, is to adjust those parameters until the greatest possible value comes forth.

And our stewardships are personal. Who else, after all, truly has access to the context parameters of our life. I've made the point that our context parameters include inflow, outflow, structure, and mind. Where our physical health is concerned, inflow includes things like the food we eat, the books we read, the movies we see, and so on. Outflow includes whether or not we exercise, how we eliminate wastes, how we talk, how we act, and so on. Whose job is it to make such choices? And if *we* don't make them, who will?

People occasionally try to rob us of our stewardship. Danny Mast held stewardship responsibility for his son, Amos, and the local medical authorities wanted to take it away. Mast did all he could to retain it, but lost it in court on entirely philosophical grounds. The philosophical point involved was the premise (which the judge accepted) that scientists, by virtue of their training, know more about what ordinary people should do than the people themselves. Classical science doesn't include the concept of personal stewardship and insists instead that all order must be imposed from the outside. Contextual healing returns the stewardship to us.

Sometimes even contextual healers don't understand

the concept of stewardship. I deal with many contextual healers, and I sometimes hear them talking about some new "breakthrough" that differs from medicine only by being based on a plant or a nutrient instead of a drug. Philosophically, however, they talk in these instances like classical scientists—as if the new breakthrough is absolutely the *only* thing a person needs. That's nonsense, of course, and while we may seek the counsel of experts and rely on products related to the parameter's we're trying to adjust, our stewardships will always include *all* of the context parameters that affect us—in particular, the context parameters that have to do with how we choose to live. And the idea that some *single* factor is all we need (whether medical or natural) isn't backed by an ounce of sense.

For these reasons, postulate two says that we have a *personal* stewardship to create the conditions of health for ourselves and for our families, and it is a stewardship that no one (though some may try) can ever completely take away.

Third Postulate: To guide us in our personal stewardships, we have been endowed with an innate capacity for discerning beauty and truth.

This postulate also contradicts classical science, which says we can't intuitively discern what's true. Yet one of our most respected scientists, Steven Jay Gould, wrote an article that shows we have tremendous intuitive powers. Gould is a paleontologist, which means he studies fossils and ancient life-forms, but the article I'm referring to is one that he wrote about Mickey Mouse.

In the article, Gould showed that Mickey Mouse has gradually changed over the years since he was first drawn. Each of the changes—larger eyes, larger head, smaller snout, etc.—have made him more childlike, to which we humans naturally respond in a very particular way: "When we see a living creature with babyish features," Gould says, "we feel an automatic surge of disarming tenderness."[2]

That surge of tenderness doesn't come from our rational minds. We discern a *pattern* and respond spontaneously to it. Who is to say that in our response to infants we aren't discerning a measure of beauty and truth?

With a little experience, even the most ordinary sandlot outfielder can break into a run at the crack of a bat and, without changing course or breaking stride, catch the ball at the exact point where its arc reaches the ground. And by the time we're adults, we can *instantly* tell when shapes aren't natural, because they just don't "look right" to our intuitive minds.

I've already cited examples like the computerized sight device (the one that presses a pattern into the blind person's back) and G. M. Stratton's seeing his upside-down world get turned right side up. These examples clearly show mental powers that transcend logic, and if they don't show ordinary people *discerning truth* (the fact that the floor belonged at the bottom of Stratton's view and the fact that what the blind people "saw" was in front of them), what do they show?

When chimpanzees and monkeys get sick, they *intuitively* discern which healing plants they ought to eat. That, at least, is the conclusion of a well-documented article published recently in *Science News*. If chimpanzees can discern such a "truth," might we not do as well?

When we start to get sick, don't we know it in an instant, even before scientific instruments can pick it up? This is why we can sometimes go to doctors with a health complaint and get told, "There's nothing wrong with you." And thanks to the classical scientific distrust of the intuitive human mind, people who feel bad but don't show objective signs of it sometimes get sent to psychiatrists on the premise that they're imagining something that's not real.

When we use our intuitive mind, it's called *discerning*. One of the main messages of contextual science is that nature isn't always rational, so we won't always be able to figure things out. But given enough experience, we can always *discern* what's true—by immersing ourselves in the richness of life and then trusting what we sense to be right.

Fourth Postulate: By following our innate capacity for discerning beauty and truth, we may gain wisdom, which is the greatest of all gifts.

Contextual science focuses on reproducibility, not rationality. The idea, in other words, is to discover what works, even if it doesn't make sense. Reproducibility means that once we discover something that works, we can use it over and over again.

Suppose science had taken a different course over the past two centuries. Suppose, to be specific, that the vitalists had won the great philosophic debate, and, as a consequence, nobody had ever paid enough attention to molecular details to discover that genes exist. Suppose, however, that we *did* discover how to reverse cancer—by trying out all sorts of context adjustments and noticing the ones that worked. If history had taken this course instead of the one it actually followed, we wouldn't know even the tiniest part of what we actually know today.

Yet we *would* know (hypothetically, at least) how to reverse cancer. That wouldn't be *knowledge* in the ordinary sense, because we wouldn't be able to *explain* anything. But perhaps it would be *wisdom* because we would know how to produce enduring results. And how much would that wisdom be worth?

Scientific history didn't take this contextual course, but that doesn't mean we can't take it ourselves. Our health challenges give us a perfect opportunity to adjust context parameters and notice what works. In fact, we'd have a hard time discovering what works *without* our challenges, and each new challenge simply gives us some new opportunity to work on. Over time, we might even discover our own individual principles for producing the health we seek, thus becoming "contextual scientists" in our own behalf. Challenges in other areas of our life offer us the same general opportunity.

In stating this fourth postulate, I call wisdom "the greatest of all gifts." I got that idea from two sources. One is Joseph Campbell, the mythologist who discovered a common myth that exists in all cultures. In this common myth, the hero faces a "zone unknown" and finds great treasure there. The treasure is always the same—wisdom and understanding—and, as treasures go, we may reasonably assume that it is the best there is.[3]

I rely most emphatically, however, on Proverbs 3:13-18, which says:

> Happy is the man that findeth wisdom, and the man that getteth understanding. For the merchandise of it is better than the merchandise of silver, and the gain thereof than fine gold. She is more precious than rubies: and all the things thou canst desire are not to be compared unto her. Length of days is in her right hand: and in her left hand riches and honour. Her ways are ways of pleasantness, and all her paths are peace.

> She is a tree of life to them that lay hold upon
> her: and happy is every one that retaineth her.[4]

I once looked up the word "prosperity" in that same dictionary of word origins. It comes from a Latin verb—*sperare*, which means "to hope"—coupled with the prefix *pro*, which means "toward." Prosperity, then, means "toward hope," or a hopeful way of looking at things. The opposite of prosperity is a word that couples the same hopeful root—*sperare*—with the prefix *de*, meaning "away from." The opposite of prosperity is *despair*.[5]

Despair doesn't come from not being able to explain things. It comes from not being able to produce results. Wouldn't its antidote, then, be practical wisdom rather than scientific knowledge? And if personal experience (guided, I suggest, by that "source of eternal justice" referred to in the Supreme Court decision[6]) isn't the path to practical wisdom, what is?

Fifth Postulate: In the long run, nothing can substitute for our personal stewardships.

I live at the foot of the Wasatch mountains, and during the winter, elk sometimes feed on the bushes and shrubs in a section of our town. This annoys some citizens, arouses compassion in others, and everyone argues about what to do.

One year, some of the townspeople organized a committee and proposed that we feed the elk. Here's how their president explained their position:

> We don't want to see elk starve or see them killed in depredation hunts. We also believe feeding them will keep them from damaging property [while] hunting for food.[7]

The Division of Wildlife Resources urged these people *not* to feed the elk. The Division's representative said:

> Elk are hardy animals, and they wouldn't starve
> on a winter like this. Feeding them only makes
> them more dependent year after year on artifi-
> cial feeding methods.We feel the best use of
> funds is to rejuvenate range and to acquire
> more winter range land.[8]

I believe the Division is right, and that negative feedback makes it so. When we're dealing with self-regulated systems (elk qualify, and so do we), whatever we artificially add gets spontaneously subtracted, and whatever we artificially subtract gets spontaneously added back. As a consequence, whenever we substitute for our personal stewardships, we create dependencies that end up worse than whatever we'd hoped to fix.

The elk example makes another interesting point. The people who wanted to feed the elk were driven by their *compassion*. They genuinely cared for those elk. They sometimes had a hard time seeing, however, that the people who disagreed with them *also* cared for the elk, but they had *practical* concerns as well—concerns about what works and what doesn't, and about allowing animals to be free. As a consequence of this misperception, discussions sometimes degenerated into attacks on the motives of the people who didn't think we should feed the elk. This confused the issue considerably and made it awfully hard to resolve in a reasonable way.

The medical authorities who took Amos Mast away from his parents may have been acting from their compassion for the boy. Yet they believed in their compassion (a) that their scientific decisions could take over for Mr. and Mrs. Mast's stewardship for their son, and (b) that their drugs could take over for the stewardship of Amos Mast's genes over the processes of his own body. As I mentioned, classical science doesn't include the concept of stewardship, so it's based primarily on substituting scientific authority for self-regulation whenever natural processes break down. That's what happened in the Danny Mast case, yet there's no evidence, scientific or otherwise, that (except in cases of *genuine* need) substituting for personal stewardships will *ever* work.

Sixth Postulate: Governments cannot promote the general welfare by taking over the personal stewardships of their citizens.

This, of course, is simply an extension of the fifth postulate. I mention it separately because it's such a critical issue today. Every time Congress assembles, our legislators address at least a few issues that have to do with our *personal* problems—finding work, raising children, keeping healthy, and so on. The solutions they propose generally end up in two categories: (1) solutions that *sustain* our personal stewardships and (2) solutions that *replace* our stewardships. The solutions in the second category—the ones that *replace* our stewardships—generally have government doing for us something that we can best do for ourselves.[9]

As happened in the elk case, the debates over these personal issues too often turn on motives, as if compassion were the issue instead of freedom and practicality. The stewardship-replacing programs come from the classical premise that we can impose order from the outside. The stewardship-sustaining solutions are based on the contextual premise that when order gets *imposed* on self-regulating systems, it tends to get reversed.

I've been impressed by at least one government program that recognizes negative feedback: the Forest Service's policy to let most natural forest fires burn. Negative feedback applies to forests because the growth of the forest creates conditions that *inhibit* growth: the canopy begins to block sunlight, pine needles accumulate on the forest floor, the trees become more susceptible to diseases and pests, and so on. As the forest gets older, then, it becomes both less able to grow and more susceptible to burning. This is self-inhibition—the foundation of negative feedback.

After the Yellowstone fires of the summer of 1988, the journal *Bioscience* published a series of articles on the controversy that erupted over the Forest Service's let-burn policy. One of the articles presents a bar graph showing how many acres within the fire area have burned each decade since 1690.[10] For the first nineteen decades, the graph shows repeating up-and-down cycles of moderate burning. Then, about 1880, the bars practically disappear.

The disappearing of the bars (meaning no burning, to speak of) coincides with the time when preventing forest fires became popular. Between 1880 and 1970, only four decades show burning, and then only tiny amounts. But all of a sudden, in the decade of the 1980s, the bar practically bursts through the top of the graph, almost tripling any previous decade.

It's not hard to see what happened. The graph also shows changes in four kinds of forest, based on age. For nineteen decades, the graph shows a balanced mix, with lots of young forest, modest amounts of old forest, and burning every decade but one. Then, coinciding with the fire-prevention efforts, the amount of young forest begins to decline as the amount of old forest grows. By the end of the 1970s, the old-forest line is growing upward at a forty-five degree slope, while the young-forest line has settled down to practically zero. With this forest mix, burning had by now become almost inevitable, and trying to prevent it could literally have no consequence but to allow the forest to age a little more, making it *still* more susceptible to fire and *still* less able to grow. Eventually forests must burn or die.

So what was the effect of our decades-long efforts to protect Yellowstone from fire?

> Our data indicate that the principal effect of fire suppression was to delay the onset of a major fire event, which has probably been inevitable given the nature of the fuels complex that had developed since the last extensive fires in the 1700s. . . . The fires of the late twentieth century were comparable, in total area burned, to the fires of the late seventeenth and eighteenth centuries. An important difference is that nearly all of the area burned in the most recent half-century was burned in one year rather than being spread out over a few major fire years.

The authors conclude by asking, "What may be the ecological effects?"[11] Our desire to preserve our forests is motivated by compassion, but we can't overlook negative feedback and its natural reversing.

Nobel Prize-winning economist Milton Friedman wrote an article for *Newsweek* magazine entitled "Laws that do harm"[12] In it, he says this, "There is a sure-fire way to predict the consequences of a government social program adopted to achieve worthy ends. Find out what the well-meaning, public-interested person who advocated its adoption expected it to accomplish. Then reverse those expectations. You will have an accurate prediction of actual results." Friedman went on to cite examples to justify his point and challenged his readers to show him any government successes that might contradict him. I don't know how his readers responded, but I suspect they found very little to cite.

Our current health-care laws are based on the "consumer-protection" argument, which says that government agencies, in their quest for our general welfare, should do for us something that we would otherwise do for ourselves. Those laws may have been motivated by compassion, but they overlook certain *practical* concerns—like the fact that taking over our personal stewardships (except in times of *genuine* need) can only make us weak—and they deserve a place, therefore, among Friedman's "laws that do harm."

Although the prohibitions aren't explicit, we may be prevented from applying contextual principles unless our current health laws change. Our challenge, therefore, is to elect legislators who understand that point and are willing to honor our stewardships by returning them to us.

Seventh Postulate: Through the principles of contextual healing our problems may be turned into strengths.

Human nature being what it is, we usually don't pay attention to our context parameters until we have to. And what makes us "have to" is usually a problem of some sort. In that sense, our problems are good for us. They show us what we need to work on, and they give us a chance to test various context adjustments so we can notice the ones that work. To repeat the essence of the fourth postulate, our problems are the source of our wisdom, which is the greatest of all gifts.

Accepting this fact is probably the biggest overhaul of our thinking that we have to face. We're used to complaining about our problems and cursing them as burdens that we shouldn't have to bear. In place of complaining, contextual healing suggests that we fill our hearts and minds with visions of health—visions that are as real (though unexpressed) as the problems we face. And it teaches us that we may call forth those visions if we will simply immerse ourselves in the richness of life, trust our intuitive understanding, and—by learning to adjust our context parameters—accept the stewardships that are ours.

10

Setting the Context for Change

In the health-care smorgasbord I envision, contextual healing and orthodox medicine will both play a role. Contextual healing will be the primary principle—for maintaining health and for almost all chronic care. Medicine will be the secondary principle, used temporarily when acute and traumatic events create circumstances that contextual healing can't address, and used more enduringly when genetic deficiencies or permanent injuries render contextual healing truly impossible. Contextual healing and medicine will therefore coexist—a primary principle for *sustaining* our natural processes, and a secondary principle for *replacing* them.

Principles for sustaining and replacing coexist in all other areas of life as well. Parents use contextual principles to sustain their children's healthy self-reliance, but when that self-reliance gets out of hand, they must replace it temporarily with secondary principles of a more intrusive sort. Business leaders both sustain and replace their employees' self-reliance, while governments both sustain and replace the self-reliance of their citizens. In all cases, the sustaining principles are the first resort and the long-term goal. They are primary principles because they alone allow spontaneous health. The replacing principles are secondary—for backup only—and used on those rare occasions when, by virtue of breakdown or weakness in the system itself, sustaining principles alone will fail.

We have a health-care system in which the secondary principle has usurped the primary role. We spend billions of dollars replacing natural processes whose only fault is that they have not been properly sustained. In molecular terms, we spend billions of dollars seeking drugs to replace the stewardship of the genes.

What kinds of children would we raise if parents were compelled to forever replace the stewardships of their children on the premise that the sustaining principles are unproven and unwise? What kind of businesses would we see if managers, for the same reason, could only replace the stewardships of their employees? We would very likely see both families and businesses fail.

Perhaps we shouldn't be surprised, therefore, that we are seeing our health-care system fail. The contextual principles that sustain our body's natural processes have been condemned as unproven and unwise, and the idea of *replacing* stewardships—both medically and politically—has become the order of the day.

But not without extraordinary costs. In 1965, 3 percent of employee compensation went to medical care. Today the figure is 15 percent and rising.[1] Every time an American automobile gets sold, $700 of its cost goes to pay for the medical care of the employees who built it.[2]

If we figure medical costs as a percentage of Gross National Product, we already outspend every other nation in the world.[3] If our medically oriented health-care system were a nation all by itself, its Gross National Product—without help from any other segment of our economy—would surpass the entire Gross National Product of all but five or six other nations.[4] Yet we remain tenth in maternal mortality, seventeenth in infant mortality, and nineteenth in life expectancy—hardly what our scientific superiority would lead us to expect.[5]

For those weak positions, we spent $500 billion for medical care in 1987, and if the pace of growth continues, we'll double that amount by 1995, and triple it by the year 2000.[6]

Small wonder, then, that an article published in the *Journal of the American Medical Association* reported that the American health-care system is "out of control" and called it "an enormous national problem."[7]

Health-care experts haven't been shy about recommending solutions to this problem of escalating costs. They propose, for example:

- Turning health care into a public utility.[8]
- Mandating universal health insurance.[9]
- Rationing health care.[10]
- Controlling the fees charged by physicians.[11]
- Putting more money into medical research.[12]
- Creating new forms of health-care management.[13]
- Restructuring medical training[14]
- Strengthening medical licensing regulations.[15]

But what if the problem is something that these solutions don't address? What if the problem is a simple philosophic mismatch—the fact that we've mistakenly been trying to solve our contextual breakdowns with purely molecular means? In that case, turning health care into a public utility won't help. Neither will mandating universal health insurance. And neither will any of the other proposed solutions that leave the mismatch intact. Even Lewis Thomas, one of medicine's most eloquent spokesmen, admits that "there is really little prospect [of overcoming the diseases that plague us] by mounting a still larger health-care system at still greater cost for delivering essentially today's kind of technology on a larger scale."[16]

Addressing the mismatch won't be easy, for the role of medicine will necessarily be reduced. Hundreds of thousands of families earn their livelihood through our medical enterprise. Fortunes and careers have been invested in it. Our medical system, by itself, is an economy larger than the economies of most Eastern European countries. Changing its focus won't be easy.

Those Eastern European economies are themselves struggling with change. Don't they show us in vivid and unforgettable terms that promises eventually come due and incomplete philosophies ultimately break down—especially those that are politically imposed? Could our health-care struggles be showing us the same thing?

Perhaps not. Perhaps the ideas I'm proposing are wrong. Perhaps medicine *is* the entire solution to chronic illness, and we must inevitably replace our natural processes with drugs and machines. But can we be sure of that position if we persist in condemning the contextual healing alternatives on philosophic grounds alone, without discovering through actual experience—not by the double-blind experiments of classical science, but according to *contextual* methods of discovering truth—whether or not contextual healing works?

For the moment, the mismatch remains. As a father, I still risk losing my children to medical authorities should I disagree with what they recommend. Natural products still remain practically excluded from FDA approval, and healers who practice contextual therapies still risk losing their medical licenses if they have them, and (in some states, at least) risk going to jail if they don't.

We must remedy that mismatch by creating a full and respectful partnership between the two healing models. The partnership will retain medicine's strength—its capacity to deal in heroic ways with acute illnesses, genetic deficiencies, and traumatic injuries—while complementing that strength with contextual healing for treating chronic illnesses and for maintaining long-term health.

May I suggest as a first step that we each determine individually that, as we deal with these issues, we will place truth, health, and human relationships above prestige, power, and personal gain. This would set a *context* in which the partnership between the principles can flourish. By that simple step, we will set in motion a healing. And it will be *contextual* healing of the highest sort.

References

Introduction

1. Medical historian Arturo Castiglioni calls these two philosophies (a) "techno-morphological, chiefly analytical" and (b) "cosmical, vitalistic, and synthetical." As Castiglioni notes, "these two tendencies have a point of contact and at the same time are very different. They may alternate or modify each other and at times keep each other back. Thus, analytical doctrine returns in a period in which exaggerated metaphysical tendencies render absolutely necessary a very strict control of the method of reasoning, while a synthetic tendency with its vitalistic attitude appears . . . when a system has taken the inflexibility of a program so as to acquire the authority of a dogma." A. Castiglioni, "Neo-Hippocratic tendency of contemporary medical thought," *Medical Life* 41 (1934): 127–28.

2. N. E. Davies et al., "Applying brakes to the runaway American health care system," *Journal of the American Medical Association* 263 (January 5, 1990): 73.

Chapter 1
Old Ideas, New Life

1. "I do not believe that objective observers would say that the American health service system has enhanced productivity or improved. In a recent survey, only 10 percent of the

American people expressed satisfaction with this system." Testimony by Dr. Uwe Reinhardt, President-Elect, Association for Health Services Research, Hearing before the Subcommittee on Health and the Environment of the Committee on Energy and Commerce, House of Representatives, One Hundred First Congress, First Session, on H.R. 2601, June 16, 1989, 64. Also, "Most Americans are fed up with the nation's health-care system . . . according to a new survey. The study, published in the current issue of *Health Management Quarterly* looks at attitudes toward health care in the U.S., Canada and Great Britain. Almost 90% of 1,250 adults surveyed in the U.S. said the U.S. system needs either 'fundamental change' or 'complete rebuilding.' " "Survey finds Americans are sick of U.S. medicine," *Wall Street Journal* (February 15, 1986).

2.   Susan Getzendanner, "Permanent injunction order against AMA," *Journal of the American Medical Association* 259 (January 1, 1988): 81–82.

3.   I am indebted for this example to Gregoire Nicolis and Ilya Prigogine: "Suppose now that we submit a cubic centimeter of water to the conditions that prevail during a winter storm. We will obtain an intricately patterned snowflake. . . . We see that the same system can appear in different aspects, evoking successive impressions of 'simplicity' and 'complexity.' " Gregoire Nicolis and Ilya Prigogine, *Exploring Complexity: An Introduction* (New York: W. H. Freeman, 1989), 6. James Gleick also discusses snowflakes in his book *Chaos: Making a New Science* (New York: Viking, 1987), 309–14. Entirely on my own, I've grossly oversimplified the example, and possibly even misstated it. Specifically, I use wind as one of the context parameters, but the article on snow in *The McGraw-Hill Encyclopedia of Science and Technology* doesn't assign a major role to the wind, discussing "fall velocity" instead. However, the article does say that snow crystals differ from frost crystals in that they "are ventilated by ambient wind." And it says that "they become oriented with their longest dimension horizontal by lee eddies formed by the airflow around the crystal" and refers to a "molding by aerodynamic forces as the flake falls through the air." I therefore feel at least moderately confident that wind is a context parameter in making snowflakes, although "fall velocity" might be more accurate. My decision to use wind rather than fall velocity has entirely to do with the fact that wind best suited my example. It's more vivid,

and more reasonably something we could adjust by moving a hypothetical lever. "Snow," *McGraw-Hill Encyclopedia of Science and Technology* (New York: McGraw-Hill, 1987), 16:479–81.

4. "An even more radical rethinking is called for by the consideration that the environment in which development occurs has an effect on the character of the phenotype which will be produced. This introduces a very remarkable type of logical indeterminacy into the whole system. One and the same set of genes may produce different phenotypes if they develop in different environments; or again, some differences in genotype may fail to come to expression when they develop in particular environments, so that identical phenotypes are produced." C. H. Waddington, "Evolution in the sub-human world," in E. Jantsch and C. H. Waddington, *Evolution and Consciousness: Human Systems in Transition* (Reading, MA: Addison-Wesley Publishing Company, 1976), 13.

5. Ilya Prigogine and Isabelle Stengers, *Order out of Chaos: Man's New Dialogue with Nature* (New York: Bantam Books, 1984), 19.

6. Ibid., 8.

7. Ibid., 6.

8. Ibid., 57, emphasis added.

9. M. R. Feigenbaum, "Universal behavior in nonlinear systems," in D. Campbell et al., eds., *Order in Chaos* (Amsterdam: North Holland Publishing Company, 1983), 17, emphasis added.

10. H. Haken, *Advanced Synergetics* (Berlin: Springer-Verlag, 1983), vii–viii.

11. D. Bohm, "The implicate order: A new approach to the nature of reality," in David L. Schindler, ed., *Beyond Mechanism: The Universe in Recent Physics and Catholic Thought* (Lantham, MD: University Press of America, 1986), 27, emphasis added.

12. Serra et al. call the cavity structure "an ordering principle." Roberto Serra, Massimo Andretta, and Mario Compiani, *Introduction to the Physics of Complex Systems: The Mesoscopic Approach to Fluctuations, Nonlinearity, and Self-organization* (Oxford: Pergamon Press, 1986), 3.

13. H. Haken, "Operational approaches to complex systems: An introduction," in H. Haken, ed., *Complex Systems—Operational Approaches in Neurobiology, Physics and Computers* (Berlin: Springer-Verlag, 1985), 6.

14. Ibid., 4–5.

15. Serra, Andretta, and Compiani, 145, emphasis added.

16. Prigogine and Stengers, 40.

Chapter 2
Casualties in a Philosophic War

1.   T. J. Kaptchuk, *The Web That Has No Weaver* (New York: Congdon & Weed, 1983), 18. I changed the original "looks" to "looking," and the article "a" to "the," to fit the structure of my sentence.

2.   This common natural healing principle also had its Western origins with Hippocrates: "Hippocrates uses the outward appearance of man in a healthy condition as the standard for discerning the visible signs of illness. The physician, he says, 'should observe . . . first the countenance of the patient, if it be like those of persons in health . . . this is the best of all; whereas the most opposite to it is the worst.' " "Medicine," in R. M. Hutchins et al., eds., *Great Books of the Western World* (Chicago: Encyclopaedia Britannica, 1952), 88.

3.   "Clinical observations of traditional Chinese medical approaches to 65 cases of ulcers," *Journal of Traditional Chinese Medicine* 6 (June 1959): 30–33. Also pertinent is this observation: "Peptic ulcer disease has been the subject of intense clinical and basic science research, both as to pathophysiology (the perturbation of normal physiology that leads to the anatomic fact) and as to treatment (what interventions cause the anatomic fact to disappear). Yet a major study of ulcer treatment reported in *The New England Journal of Medicine* revealed a surprising finding: the anatomic fact could not be correlated with the patient's complaint. When ulcer patients were asked to record symptom scores, these bore essentially no relationship to endoscopic findings: 'Fifty-five percent of patients whose ulcers were unhealed after four weeks, regardless of treatment group, became asymptomatic during the course of treatment.' Furthermore, 12 of 45 patients whose ulcer had healed endoscopically continued to have some ulcer symptoms. These findings led the authors to comment that 'the presence or absence of symptoms during the fourth treatment week was a poor predictor of presence or absence of an ulcer crater.' This study is frequently cited as establishing the equal efficacy of antacids and cimetidine in the treatment of peptic ulcer disease. It has recently been cited in an article questioning the efficacy of medical treatment for ulcer. Other investigators have duplicated these curious findings; yet our commitment to the disease

category peptic ulcer is undiminished." R. J. Baron, "An introduction to medical phenomenology: I can't hear you while I'm listening," *Annals of Internal Medicine* 103 (1985): 607. The article cited in this report is W. L. Peterson et al., "Healing of duodenal ulcer with an antacid regimen," *New England Journal of Medicine* 297 (August 18, 1977): 341–45.

4. David Daniel Palmer, *The Science, Art, and Philosophy of Chiropractic* (Portland, OR: Portland Printing House, 1910).

5. In some cases, a condition I've characterized as "too active" or "too calm" may be just the opposite from another perspective. For example, I put bulimia in the too-active column because bulimia sufferers eat too much. On the other hand, their overeating may be due to the fact that their sympathetic nervous system is in some fashion too weak, which may make them physically inactive to one degree or another. Amphetamines, which act as diet suppressants, serve to stimulate the sympathetic nervous system and so act as "uppers" in the sense that they provoke physical and mental arousal. From this perspective, bulimia might appear in the too-calm column with anorexia in the too-active column.

6. A. Castiglioni, *A History of Medicine* (New York: Alfred A. Knopf, 1958), 178.

7. D. L. Schindler, "Introduction: The problem of mechanism," in David L. Schindler, ed., *Beyond Mechanism: The Universe in Recent Physics and Catholic Thought* (Lantham, MD: University Press of America, 1986), 1. As his reference for the word origins, Schindler cites "Liddell and Scott Lexicon."

8. Castiglioni, 178, emphasis added.

9. P. Edwards, *Encyclopedia of Philosophy*, 10 vols. (New York: Macmillan, 1967), 4:6. Edwards also points out, however, that the Hippocratic writings are so varied that they can be claimed as support for almost anything: "Since the Corpus Hippocraticum is a collection by diverse authors, one can find in it support for a variety of principles. Bacon and Galileo quoted 'Hippocrates' as the protagonist of experiment and observation. Voltaire admitted his renunciation of an empty metaphysics. . . . Leibniz invoked Hippocrates' endorsement of the harmony and interconnection of all things. Berkeley compared Newton's physics to his teaching. The multiplication of disease entities was defended by reference to his authority, as was the insistence on including the various forms of an illness under one name. Treatment based on the

dogma of contraria contrariis (cure opposites with opposites)—
no less than that based on the dogma of similia similibus (cure
like with like)—was called Hippocratic." Despite this diversity,
however, no authority questions Hippocrates' commitment
to the existence of an innate healing power, which is my focus
here.

10. Atomism is also often attributed to Epicurus, who lived
roughly a century later. L. S. King, "Explanations of disease:
Historian's viewpoint," in H. T. Engelhardt, Jr., et al., eds.,
Evaluation and Explanation in the Biomedical Sciences (Dordrecht,
Holland: D. Reidel Publishing Company, 1975), 15.

11. Edwards, 1:193.

12. Essay on "Medicine," in R. M. Hutchins et al., eds., *Great
Books of the Western World* (Chicago: Encyclopaedia Britannica, 1986), 3:85.

13. Edwards, 1:195.

14. R. A Weinberg, "The molecules of life," in *The Molecules of
Life: Readings from Scientific American* (New York: W. H. Freeman
and Company, 1985), 9.

15. Ibid., 2, 9.

16. Cited and referenced in Harris Coulter, *Divided Legacy: The
Conflict Between Homoeopathy and the American Medical Association*, 2d ed. (Richmond, CA: North Atlantic Books, 1982), 54.

17. "Kepler's empirical formulation of the laws of planetary
motion represents some sixty man-years of research (thirty
years of Tycho Brahe's observations and thirty years of Kepler's
arithmetic analysis), whereas Newton's derivation took only
an hour or two. Moreover, this derivation from the law of
gravity shows that Kepler's version of the third law is slightly
incorrect and replaces Kepler's approximate statement of the
third law by its correct statement." J. H. Weaver, ed., *The
World of Physics: A Small Library of the Literature of Physics from
Antiquity to the Present*, 3 vols. (New York: Simon and Schuster,
1987), 1:19.

18. B. Fagan, "Dating by solar eclipse," *Archaeology* 42 (Septem-
ber/October 1989): 20–23.

19. Genesis 1:26.

20. Ilya Prigogine and Isabelle Stengers quote this paean to
Newton and attribute it to "Ampère's son," probably referring to the son of the French physicist and mathematician,
André Marie Ampère, whose name now represents the basic
unit of electrical current. I. Prigogine and I. Stengers, *Order*

out of Chaos: Man's New Dialogue with Nature (New York: Bantam Books, 1984), 67.

21. Cited in ibid., 47.
22. M. A. B. Brazier, *A History of Neurophysiology in the 19th Century* (New York: Raven Press, 1988), 78.
23. M. A. B. Brazier, *A History of Neurophysiology in the 17th and 18th Centuries: From Concept to Experiment* (New York: Raven Press, 1984), 83.
24. Ibid., 64.
25. Ibid., 78.
26. Ibid., 25.
27. Ibid., 80.
28. Ibid., 109.
29. Ibid., 173.
30. Ibid., 1.
31. Brazier, *A History of Neurophysiology in the 19th Century*, 219.
32. Ibid., 80.
33. Ibid., 98.
34. Ibid., 42.
35. "The dispute between ontological and physiological theories of disease turns centrally on the ontological and logical status of disease entities. Ontological theories framed views within which diseases could be appreciated as specific entities. Physiological theorists framed views within which diseases could be appreciated as particular deviations from general regularities. In the first case, the accent of reality fell upon the disease; in the second case the accent fell upon the individual and his circumstances. . . . Physiologists have been willing to speak of diseases and accord them a conceptual reality. . . . But reality was close to that of the physiological theorists in being etiologically open—disease entities did not prove to have unique etiologies. As Virchow indicated, known pathogens can exist in hosts without pathology. Disease causality is equivocal. Diseases are, as the physiological nosologists stressed, much more complex than the easy simplicity implicit in many ontological nosologies. Diseases are, in fact, not only multifactorial, but multidimensional, involving genetic, physiological, psychological, and sociological components." Medicine, nonetheless, has adopted the ontological point of view. T. H. Engelhardt, "The concepts of health and disease," in T. H. Engelhardt et al., *Evaluation and Explanation in the Biomedical Sciences* (Dordrecht, Holland: D. Reidel Publishing Company,

1975), 131–32.

36. R. P. Hudson, *Disease and Its Control* (Westport, CT: Green-wood Press, 1983), 229.

37. Ibid., 236.

38. Tree structure example taken from: *Medical Subject Headings–Tree Subjects, 1988* (Bethesda, MD: National Library of Medicine, 1988).

39. "Too little is known about the condition and . . . what is known is inadequate and inconsistent. Therefore, adding the category to an official classification of mental disorders, with specified criteria, may seem premature and likely to promote a false sense of knowledge." R. L. Spitzer et al., "Late luteal phase dysphoric disorder and DSM-III-R." *American Journal of Psychiatry* 146 (July 1989): 894.

40. For a complete discussion of this controversy, see ibid.

41. Eric W. Martin, *Hazards of Medication* (Philadelphia: J. B. Lippincott Company, 1978), 3.

42. Cited in J. D. Allan et al., "Challenging the focus on technology: A critique of the medical model in a changing health care system," *Advances in Nursing Science* 10 (1988): 28.

Chapter 3
Blind Spots in the Classical View

1. *Reader's Digest Illustrated Encyclopedic Dictionary*, 2 vols. (Pleasantville, NY: Reader's Digest Association, 1987), 1:491.

2. John Briggs and F. David Peat discuss Poincarè's discovery under the heading, "Newton Fell, and No One Noticed." John Briggs and F. David Peat, *Turbulent Mirror* (New York: Harper & Row, 1989), 26–29.

3. Ilya Prigogine and Isabelle Stengers, *Order out of Chaos: Man's New Dialogue with Nature* (New York: Bantam Books, 1984), 29.

4. Cited in Briggs and Peat, 149.

5. Ibid.

6. "If a negative sign is assigned to energy which is delivered to the surroundings, the influx of heat is Q, while the work on or produced by the system is A. There exists a variable of state, the internal energy U, which combines these two parameters in this equations: $\Delta U = \Delta Q + \Delta A$." I. Lamprecht, "Application of the concepts of classical thermodynamics in biology," in Ingolf Lamprecht and A. I. Zotin, eds., Thermodynamics of Biological Processes (Berlin: Walter de Gruy-

ter, 1978), 5.

7.   "When we are dealing with . . . systems far from equilibrium, we know that these systems must be in a rather strong interaction with their environment. That means we must supply the systems with a sufficiently strong influx of energy and matter, so that they can acquire new states, say, at a higher level of order. But this requires that we . . . have a pronounced exchange of energy with the surrounding." H. Haken, "Synergetics, its microscopic and macroscopic foundation," in G. Caglioti and H. Haken, eds., *Synergetics and Dynamic Instabilities* (Amsterdam: North Holland Publishing Company, 1988), 18.

8.   Prigogine and Stengers, 177, emphasis added.

9.   Gregoire Nicolis and Ilya Prigogine, *Exploring Complexity: An Introduction* (New York: W. H. Freeman, 1989), 50.

10.   "In short, we arrive at a simple, appealing picture of how order can emerge in a system. In somewhat anthropomorphic terms, order appears to be a compromise between two antagonists: the nonlinear chemicallike process . . . and the transportlike process. . . . Disturbing the delicate balance between these two competing actors leads to such qualitative changes as an erratic state in which each element of the system acts on its own; or, on the contrary, a 'homeostatic' fossillike state in which the fluctuations are crushed and a full uniformity is imposed. Complexity, therefore, appears to be limited on opposite sides by different kinds of states of disorder. It is difficult to avoid the feeling that this conclusion, which follows from quite general laws governing the dynamics of physico-chemical systems, should provide valuable clues for modeling systems that are beyond the realm of physics and chemistry." Nicolis and Prigogine, 170–171.

11.   Photo credit: Brig Cabe/Insight.

12.   I. R. Epstein, "Chemical oscillations and nonlinear chemical dynamics," in Erica Jen, ed., *1989 Lectures in Complex Systems* (Redwood City, CA: Addison Wesley Publishing Company, 1990), 226.

13.   "The conditions for the onset of such structures are: (1) The system must be open and subject to the constant input and output of matter and energy. This fact implies that chemical, biochemical and hydrodynamic systems must be kept far from thermodynamic equilibrium. (2) Various catalytic, cross-catalytic, or feedback processes must be present in the system.

This fact insures the description of the system in terms of non-linear differential equations. (3) For well-defined values of imposed constraints [i.e., the context parameters], the homogeneous steady state can no longer damp the small fluctuations present in all environments and new organized and stable states appear in the system." A. Babloyantz, "Selforganization in Biosystems," in Horst Kleinkauf et al., eds., *The Roots of Modern Biochemistry* (Berlin: Walter de Gruyter, 1988), 925.

14.   Nicolis and Prigogine, 18.

15.   The word "spontaneous" comes from a Latin root, *spontaneus,* which means "of one's own free will." Eric Partridge, *Origins: A Short Etymological Dictionary of Modern English*, 4th ed. (New York: Macmillan Publishing, 1966), 654.

16.   A. Bartloff, "Electrical activity of intestine recorded with pressure electrode," *American Journal of Physiology* 201 (1961): 209–12. Cited and interpreted from the perspective of contextual science in Leon Glass and Michael C. Mackey, *From Clocks to Chaos: The Rhythms of Life* (Princeton, NJ: Princeton Univ. Press, 1988), 83. In a similar vein, molecular biologist Gilbert N. Ling proposes that potassium and sodium represent context parameters and that their balance affects the body's cellular rhythms in critical and important ways. He also cites evidence showing that ATP helps maintain that balance. G. N. Ling, "The living state according to the association-induction hypothesis," in R. K. Mishra, ed., *The Living State* (New York: John Wiley & Sons, 1984), 21-34. Henry T. Randall also describes the dangerous effects of hypokalemia (low potassium) and hyperkalemia (high potassium) on the rhythms of the heart. H. T. Randall, "Water, electrolytes, and acid-base balance," in Maurice E. Shils and Vernon R. Young, eds., *Modern Nutrition in Health and Disease,* 7th ed. (Philadelphia: Lea & Febiger, 1988), 130-33. The National Research Council's Committee on Diet and Health points out that "diets with a high sodium content tend to be low in potassium, whereas those with high potassium have a low sodium content," which may help explain salt's generally harmful effects. National Research Council (U.S.), Committee on Diet and Health, *Diet and Health: Implications for Reducing Chronic Disease Risk* (Washington, DC: National Academy Press, 1989), 424.

17.   Prigogine and Stengers, 156–59.

18.   S. Hart, "Mystery amoeba: Parasitologists struggle to decipher

a puzzling microbe's true identity," *Science News* 136 (September 30, 1989): 216–19.

19. See Barbara McClintock, *The Discovery and Characterization of Transposable Elements: The Collected Papers of Barbara McClintock* (New York: Garland Publishing, 1987).

20. P. Herrlich et al., "The mammalian genetic stress response," *Advances in Enzyme Regulation* 25 (1986): 485–504.

21. P. Herrlich et al., "Genetic changes in mammalian cells reminiscent of an SOS response," *Human Genetics* 67 (1984): 360–68.

22. G. K. Scott et al., "Differential amplification of antifreeze protein genes in the pleuronectinae," *Journal of Molecular Evolution* 27 (1988): 29–35.

23. R. P. Hudson, *Disease and Its Control* (Westport, CT: Greenwood Press, 1983), 242.

24. "The first, or catabolic, block consists of the degradative pathways by which carbon, energy, and sometimes nitrogen, sulfur, and phosphorus are made available. . . . The second, or anabolic, block amalgamates hundreds of biosynthetic reaction sequences that generate small molecules, some common to all cells and others confined to but a few: amino acids, nucleotides, lipids, sugars, steroids, pigments, antibiotics, and pheromones." Franklin M. Harold, *The Vital Force: A Study of Bioenergetics* (New York: W. H. Freeman and Company, 1986), 28.

25. "[In PMS,] the frequency, amplitude, and patterns of pulsations of hormones may contain as much regulatory information as the plasma [blood] level of the hormone." D. R. Rubinow et al., "Models for the development and expression of symptoms in premenstrual syndrome," *Psychiatric Clinics of North America* 12 (March 1989): 56. Also, "[PMS symptoms] may result from a temporary impairment of homeostasis . . . triggered by a differential pace and magnitude of change-over-time in levels of several hormones and other substances." U. Halbreich et al., "Premenstrual changes. Impaired hormonal homeostasis," *Psychiatric Clinics of North America* 12 (March 1989): 173.

26. "The author reviewed available data from the literature related to the presence of biological rhythms in human tumor markers. Those rhythms appeared as specific criterion of underlying malignancy (CEA, ferritin); the reappearance of 'normal' rhythmicity after therapy could also reflect the

favorable outcome of the disease." C. Focan, "Chronobiology and biochemical markers of human cancer," *Pathologie Biologie* 35 (June 1987): 951.

27. For example, Glass and Mackey mention schizophrenia, Parkinson's disease, sleeping disorders, bradycardia and tachycardia, migraine headaches, and aplastic anemia. Glass and Mackey, 80, 111, 140, 160, 166, 181.

28. Ibid., 3.

29. Cited in ibid., 173.

30. Ibid.

31. Ibid., 16.

32. See E. S. Crelin, "Chiropractic," in Douglas Stalker and Clark Glymour, eds., *Examining Holistic Medicine* (Buffalo, NY: Prometheus Books, 1985), 245–72.

33. W. T. Jarvis, "Chiropractic: A skeptical view," *The Skeptical Inquirer* 12 (Fall 1987): 49.

34. "At the cellular level, strong inhomogeneities are also observed. For instance, the concentration of potassium ions, $K+$, inside the neurons, the cells of the nervous system, is higher than in the outside environment while the opposite is true for sodium ions, $Na+$. Such inequalities, *which imply states of high nonequilibrium*, are at the origin of processes, such as the conduction of the nerve impulse, which play an important role in life. They are maintained by active transport and bioenergetic reactions like glycolysis or respiration." Nicolis and Prigogine, 32, emphasis added.

35. Cited in A. C. Scott et al., "The soliton: A new concept in applied science," *Proceedings of the IEEE* 61 (October 1973): 1443.

36. More precisely, "Solitary waves occur . . . on propagating systems that are characterized by nonlinearity and dissipation. Again a balance obtains but in this case it is between the release of stored energy by the nonlinearity and its consumption by the propagating disturbance. The simplest example is probably a candle." Ibid,, 1444, emphasis added.

37. A. C. Scott, "Dynamics of Davydov solitons," *Physical Review* 26 (July 1982): 590.

38. A. S. Davydov, "Solitons in molecular system," *Physica Scripta* 20 (1979): 387–94.

39. A. C. Scott, "Coupled solitary waves in neurophysics," *Physica Scripta* 20 (1979): 395–401.

40. "At a certain pump power, called laser threshold, a complete-

ly new phenomenon occurs. An unknown demon seems to let the atomic antennas oscillate in phase. They emit now a single giant wavetrack whose length is, say, 300,000 km! The emitted light intensity, (i.e., the output power) increases drastically with further increasing input power." H. Haken, *Synergetics: An Introduction* (Berlin: Springer-Verlag, 1983), 5.

41. The complete quote refers to "the existence of a particular cavity structure (shape, dimensions, presence of mirrors, etc.) which defines the boundary conditions and functions as an 'ordering principle', as a 'suggestion' for a certain mode of organisation." Roberto Serra, Massimo Andretta, and Mario Compiani, *Introduction to the Physics of Complex Systems: The Mesoscopic Approach to Fluctuations, Nonlinearity, and Self-organization* (Oxford: Pergamon Press, 1986), 3.

42. S. Lundqvist et al., eds., *Order and Chaos in Nonlinear Physical Systems* (New York: Plenum Press, 1988), 175.

43. "At ELF, a striking range of biological interactions has been described in experiments where control procedures appear to have been adequately considered and where tissue electric gradients are in the range of fractions of mV cm-1. Thus, they do not appear to originate in classical processes of events. Although they are most often described in marine vertebrates, there is an increasing range of apparently reliable reports in mammals, including man." Cited in Scott, "Coupled solitary waves," 400, emphasis added.

44. "Over the past decade a rather impressive amount of experimental evidence has been accumulating to indicate that living organisms are behaviorally sensitive to low-intensity e.m. radiation which raises tissue temperature only by 'orders of magnitude less than 0.1° C.' Proteinaceous material on cell membrane surfaces appears to be the site of detection, and it is clear that nonlinear mechanisms must be invoked to explain the extraordinary sensitivity observed. One such nonlinear mechanism is the influence of e.m. fields on the dynamics of Davydov solitons that play functional roles in vital processes of energy transport." Scott, "Dynamics of Davydov solitons," 590.

45. James Gleick, *Chaos: Making a New Science* (New York: Viking, 1987), 79. In the original, the verb is "violated"—in past tense.

46. Briggs and Peat, 23.

47. D. Campbell et al., eds., *Order in Chaos* (Amsterdam: North Holland Publishing Company, 1983), vii.

48.   B. J. West et al., "Physiology in fractal dimension," *American Scientist* 75 (July-August 1985): 361.

Chapter 4
The Coupling of Body and Mind

1.   A. Routtenberg, ed., *Biology of Reinforcement: Facets of Brain-Stimulation Reward* (New York: Academic Press, 1980), 3.
2.   C. V. Van Toller, *The Nervous Body: An Introduction to the Autonomic Nervous System and Behaviour* (New York: John Wiley & Sons, 1979), 111.
3.   "Fertile faster, if herd under the roar," *Science News* 133 (January 9, 1988): 24.
4.   S. Rose, *The Conscious Brain* (New York: Vintage Books, 1976), 289.
5.   J. A. Treichel, "How emotions affect involuntary nerves," *Science News* 124 (September 17, 1983): 182.
6.   R. J. Rodgers, *Endorphins, Opiates and Behavioural Processes* (New York: John Wiley & Sons, 1988), 123.
7.   Ibid., 122.
8.   R. Restak, *The Brain: The Last Frontier* (New York: Warner Books, 1979), 328.
9.   W. J. Freeman et al., "Spatial EEG patterns, non-linear dynamics and perception: The Neo-Sherrington view," *Brain Research Reviews* 10 (1985): 147-75.
10.   R. W. McCarley, "Mechanisms and models of behavioral state control," in J. A. Hobson and M. A. B. Brazier, eds., *The Reticular Formation Revisited: Specifying Function for a Nonspecific System* (New York: Raven Press, 1980), 381.
11.   Scientists can produce the same two phases electrically, by stimulating a part of the brain called the hippocampus. Low-voltage stimulation provokes the synchronized rhythms of habituation. High-voltage stimulation produces the desynchronized rhythms of the orienting reflex. A precise transition boundary separates the two. T. Radil-Weiss, "Evidence for a system inhibiting reticulo-septo-hippocampal activity," in Hobson and Brazier, 408.
12.   J. Campbell, *Grammatical Man: Information, Entropy, Language, and Life* (New York: Simon and Schuster, 1982), 15-31.
13.   Ibid., 18-19.
14.   "Most striking of all, Shannon's expression for the amount of

information, the first precise, scientific measure, the first satisfactory definition of this distinctively twentieth-century commodity, was of the same form as the equation devised many years earlier, in the nineteenth century, for that most peculiar and fugitive of physical laws, the entropy principle.... That equation was a mathematical expression of the tendency for all things to become less orderly when left to themselves; for energy to undergo certain transformations in the natural course of events, making it more disorganized and not so useful, degrading its quality without diminishing its quantity." Ibid., 18. However, Shannon's information theory differs from contextual science in that it does not consider distance from equilibrium, and therefore deals only with linear processes: "The conventional, mathematically elaborated information theory founded by Claude Shannon and Warren Weaver is primarily geared to equilibrium and the stabilization of structures. Just as in Boltzmann's thermodynamic ordering principle there is only one direction possible, the direction toward equilibrium structures, in the theory by Shannon and Weaver new information is also primarily considered to reconfirm and strengthen existing information structures. The amount of information is given; it can only decrease due to the inevitable noise effect, as in equilibrium thermodynamics order can only decrease." Erich Jantsch, *The Self-organizing Universe: Scientific and Human Implications of the Emerging Paradigm of Evolution* (Oxford: Pergamon Press, 1980), 51. Also, "information theory, which Claude Shannon formulated soon after the Second World War and which contributed greatly to the development of the study of deviation-counteracting feedback systems, was trapped in a classificational epistemology which sees a structure as consisting of elements which tend to behave independently. . . . In this epistemology, structures tend to decay to more probable nonstructures. All Shannon could do was to combat this decay by means of deviation-counteracting feedback systems. Therefore, in Shannon's formulation, evolution and growth of structures were impossible, or so highly improbable that they had to be attributed to something beyond this theory." M. Maruyama, "Mutual causality and social process," in Erich Jantsch and Conrad Waddington, eds., *Evolution and Consciousness: Human Systems in Transition* (London: Addison-Wesley Publishing Company, 1976), 201. Thus while Shannon's formulations captured one small element of the relationship between information and energy, they also ignored distance from equilibrium, and thus fell far short of the advances introduced by contextual science.

15. J. T. Edsall et al., *Biothermodynamics: The Study of Biochemical Processes at Equilibrium* (New York: John Wiley & Sons, 1983), 11, emphasis added.

16. Franklin M. Harold, *The Vital Force: A Study of Bioenergetics* (New York: W. H. Freeman and Company, 1986, 474.

17. Ibid., 19, emphasis added.

18. Ibid., 34, emphasis added.

19. Ibid., 474.

20. A. B. Scheibel, "Session chairman's overview: Anatomical and physiological substrates of arousal," in Hobson and Brazier, 62.

21. R. G. Grenell et al., *Biological Foundations of Psychiatry*, 2 vols. (New York: Raven Press, 1976), 1:85.

22. Harold, 474, emphasis added.

23. For an intriguing discussion of the physical correlates of our emotions, see Melvin Konner, *The Tangled Wing: Biological Constraints on the Human Spirit* (New York: Holt, Rinehart, and Winston, 1982.

24. Restak, 117.

25. "After a relatively few hours of practice, using active head movements in 'viewing,' the subject becomes unaware of the abdominal stimulation via the electrodes and instead 'projects' images as arising from within the spaces scanned by his camera 'eye.' It is essential that the individual actively direct the camera, by head or hand movements, in order for his subjective experience to project 'real objects, out there.' " Grenell, 1:81.

26. Robert B. Livingston points out that centers for go/no go decisions exist in the reticular formation, and that the same centers, based on the time scale involved, govern both conscious and unconscious release of behavior. For example, deciding to play tennis is conscious. Deciding to go after a tough shot in the heat of a game is not, or at least depends on a different level of consciousness. In any case, our inner resources mobilize themselves according to such go/no go decisions. Robert B. Livingston, "Sensory processing, perception, and behavior," in ibid., 1:66.

27. J. W. Grau, "Activation of the opioid and non-opioid anal-

gesic systems: Evidence for a memory hypothesis and against the coulometric hypothesis," *Journal of Experimental Psychology: Animal Behavior Processes* 13 (July 1987): 215–25.

28. Described in J. B. Watson, *Psychology from the Standpoint of a Behaviourist* (Dover, NH: Frances Pinter, 1983), 241–46.
29. See R. E. Meyer et al., eds., *The Heroin Stimulus: Implications for the Theory of Addiction* (New York: Plenum Medical Book Company, 1979).
30. L. S. Harris, ed., *Problems of Drug Dependence, 1983* (Rockville, MD: National Institute on Drug Abuse, Department of Health and Human Services, 1984), 40.
31. B. Bower, "Cutting immunity with chemotherapy cues," *Science News* 137 (April 28, 1990): 262.
32. I should probably thank my mother for this. According to an article in *USA Today*, research has shown that people who ate processed lunch meats as children are more likely to get colon cancer as adults. *USA Today* 117 (February 1989), 6.
33. Karl H. Pribram, *Languages of the Brain* (Englewood Cliffs, NJ: Prentice-Hall, 1971), 91.
34. *Tzultak'a* is the name of the god of valleys and hills in the Maya Kekchi tradition. From a manuscript in the author's possession.
35. Grenell, 1:76.
36. Routtenberg, 13.
37. Restak, 27.
38. Ibid., 28.
39. S. S. Steiner et al., "Escape from self-produced rates of brain stimulation," *Science* 163 (October 24, 1963): 90–91.
40. Cited in K. H. Pribram, "Cognition and performance: The relation to neural mechanisms of consequence, confidence, and competence," in Routtenberg, 27.
41. See, for example, S. F. Maier et al., "The opioid/non-opioid nature of stress-induced analgesia and learned helplessness," *Journal of Experimental Psychology: Animal Behavior Processes* 9 (January 1983): 80–90.
42. R. C. Drugen et al., "Shock controllability and the nature of stress-induced analgesia," *Behavioral Neuroscience* 99 (October 1985): 791–801.
43. See, for example, D. Jefferys et al., "Glucocorticoids, adrenal medullary opioids, and the retention of a behavioral response after stress," *Endocrinology* 121 (September 1987): 1006–9. Also the pioneering work of Hans Selye, *The Stress of Life,*

rev. ed. (New York: McGraw-Hill Book, 1976).

44.   From an interview with Paul McLean in J. Hooper and D.
       Teresi, *Three-Pound Universe* (New York: Macmillan Publishing
       Company, 1986), 46.

45.   Cited in A. Baum et al., "Unemployment stress: Loss of
       control, reactance and learned helplessness," *Social Science and
       Medicine* 22 (1986): 509–16.

46.   Ibid.

47.   B. van der Kolk et al., "Inescapable shock, neurotransmitters,
       and addiction to trauma: Toward a psychobiology of post-
       traumatic stress," *Biological Psychiatry* 20 (March 1985): 314–25.

48.   Cited in T. Melnechuk, "Emotions, brain, immunity, and
       health: A review," in M. Clynes et al., eds., *Emotions and
       Psychopathology* (New York: Plenum Press, 1988), 200–202.

49.   Livingston, 1:84.

50.   Walter Rudolf Hess, *Biological Order and Brain Organization*
       (Berlin: Springer-Verlag, 1981), 103.

51.   See, for example, I. I. Blekhmann, *Synchronization in Science and
       Technology* (New York: ASME Press, 1988), 179.

52.   This once discredited idea has spawned a complete new
       discipline called "psychoneuroimmunology." For a recent
       general review, see Norman Cousins, *Head First: The Biology
       of Hope* (New York: E. P. Dutton, 1989).

Chapter 5
Explaining Cancer: Context or Genes?

1.   "There has been a tendency to think of the initiating event
       in chemical carcinogenesis in terms of simple random point
       mutations resulting from errors in the replication of damaged
       DNA." M. E. Lambert et al., "Inducible cellular responses
       to DNA damage in mammalian cells," in D. M. Shankel et
       al., eds., *Antimutagenesis and Anticarcinogenesis Mechanisms*
       (New York: Plenum Press, 1986), 291. See also I. B. Weinstein,
       "Current concepts and controversies in chemical carcino-
       genesis," *Journal of Supramolecular Structure and Cellular
       Biochemistry* 17 (1981): 101.

2.   Lambert, 291.

3.   E. Farber, "Pre-cancerous steps in carcinogenesis: Their physio-
       logical adaptive nature," *Biochimica et Biophysica Acta* 738
       (1984): 173.

4.   Lambert, 292, emphasis added.

5.   "In humans . . . the process often takes 10, 20, or 30 years
        before the manifestations of malignancy appear. In experimen-
        tal animals, a comparable segment of the normal life span
        ($\frac{1}{2}$ to $\frac{2}{3}$) is often required." Farber, 172.
6.   "A major principle in studies on mechanisms of carcinogenesis
        is that the process proceeds through multiple discernible
        stages." I. B. Weinstein, "The origins of human cancer:
        Molecular mechanisms of carcinogenesis and their implica-
        tions for cancer prevention and treatment. Twenty-seventh
        G. H. A. Clowes Memorial Award Lecture," *Cancer Research*
        (October 4, 1988): 4135.
7.   "We are considering very rare genetic changes, two or even
        three of which would be required for carcinogenesis, while
        the process in fact occurs with relatively high frequency." P.
        Herrlich et al., "The mammalian genetic stress response,"
        Advances in Enzyme Regulation 25 (1986): 500.
8.   Lambert, 305, emphasis added.
9.   Weinstein, "The origins of human cancer," 4137.
10.   "The Biological Sciences," in *Encyclopaedia Britannica,* 29
        vols. (Chicago: Encyclopaedia Britannica, 1988), 14:921, 936.
11.   See, for example, Walmor C. DeMello, *Cell Intercommuni-
        cation* (Boca Raton, FL: CRC Press, 1990).
12.   "Mystery amoeba," *Science News* 136 (September 30, 1989): 216.
13.   Ilya Prigogine and Isabelle Stengers, *Order out of Chaos: Man's
        New Dialogue with Nature* (New York: Bantam House, 1984),
        120.
14.   "All body cells are obligate aerobes [oxygen users], whereas all
        cancer cells are partial anaerobes. . . . Oxygen, the donor of
        energy in plants and animals, is dethroned in the cancer cells
        and replaced by an energy-yielding reaction of the lowest
        living forms, namely a fermentation of glucose." Sigismund
        Peller, *Cancer Research Since 1900: An Evaluation* (New York:
        Philosophical Society, 1979), 42. After this transformation,
        oxygen simply makes cancer cells more lethal: "Oxygen-starved
        cancer cells from mice increase their deadliness when flooded
        with oxygen in the lab and then injected into healthy mice."
        K. A. Fackelmann, "Oxygen plays a role in cancer aggressive-
        ness," *Science News* 137 (March 17, 1990): 166.
15.   Franklin M. Harold, *The Vital Force: A Study of Bioenergetics*
        (New York: W. H. Freeman and Company, 1986), 94, em-
        phasis added.

16. In the original quote, Szent-Györgyi referred to "the oxidative α state" and "the fermentative β state." I deleted the Greek symbols to make the statement easier to read. Cited from Szent-Györgyi's book *Electronic Biology and Cancer* in Kenneth R. Pelletier, *From Stress to Optimum Health* (New York: Delacorte Press, 1979), 117.
17. Ibid.
18. Ibid.
19. Cited in J. L. Oschman, "Structure and properties of ground substances," *American Zoologist* 24 (1984): 211.
20. Ibid.
21. See the entry on Virchow, *Encyclopaedia Britannica,* 29 vols. (Chicago: Encyclopaedia Britannica, 1988), 12:385.
22. C. H. Waddington, "Cancer and the theory of organizers," *Nature* (April 20, 1935): 606-7.
23. "Cancer can be induced experimentally by disturbing the normal homeostatic relations among and between cells, tissues, and organs. None of the methods used involves the use of carcinogens in the conventional sense." H. Rubin, "Cancer as a dynamic developmental disorder," *Cancer* 45 (July 1985): 2940. Also, "The ability to induce tumors by disrupting the hierarchical ordering [context] raises the question that spontaneous tumors might be initiated by similar perturbations. Genomic alterations such as chromosomal deviations or oncogene activation could be adaptive responses." P. A. Tsonis, "Embryogenesis and carcinogenesis: Order and disorder," *Anticancer Research* 7 (1985): 622.
24. Lambert, 292.
25. E. Farber, "The multistep nature of cancer development," *Cancer Research* 44 (October 1984): 4218.
26. Lambert, 302.
27. P. J. Rosch, "Stress and cancer," in Cary L. Cooper, ed., *Psychosocial Stress and Cancer* (Chichester, England: John Wiley & Sons Ltd., 1984), 38.
28. "The topographical relations in a tissue can be disturbed by implanting into connective tissue of the rat rectangles of chemically inert plastic, metal foil, or glass coverslips. As long as the implanted material exceeds a size of 1 sq. cm. and remains intact for 6 months, sarcomas develop along the noncontiguous surfaces of the connective tissue. If the inert material is perforated, the incidence of tumors is reduced;

if it is inserted in the form of a finely divided powder or a textile mesh, no tumors occur. Since the latter treatments greatly increase the surface of material available to cells, a chemical mechanism is ruled out." Rubin, 2936.

29.   R. T. Schimke, "Methotrexate resistance and gene amplification," *Cancer* 57 (May 1986): 1912.
30.   They carry such names as gene amplification (Herrlich, 496), gene rearrangements (Lambert 291), sequence deletions (ibid., 293), and chromosomal transformations (Weinstein, "The origins of human cancer," 4137). They have the effect of "profoundly altering the economy of the . . . cell." E. M. Witkin, "The SOS response: Implications for cancer," in J. Michael Bishop, Janet Rowley, and Mel Greaves, eds., *Genes and Cancer* (New York: Alan R. Liss, 1984), 99.
31.   R. E. Kellems et al., "Amplified dihydrofolate reductase genes are located in chromosome regions containing DNA that replicates during the first half of the S-phase," *Journal of Cell Biology* 92 (February 1982): 531–39.
32.   "These findings provide a clear demonstration of a recurring theme in cancer biology—i.e., that the phenotypic properties of tumor cells preexist but lie dormant in the normal tissue of origin." Weinstein, "Current concepts and controversies in chemical carcinogenesis," 106. Also, "It has thus been established that embryonic cells often produce a series of gene products which after birth are replaced by another set of gene products. In the normal adult, these fetal gene products are not expressed again in large amounts. They often become re-expressed, however, in some diseases, and especially in neoplasia [cancer], in the adult." F. Jacob, "Expression of embryonic characters by malignant cells," in *Fetal Antigens and Cancer,* Ciba Foundation Symposium 96 (London: Pitman, 1983), 5.
33.   "One of the strongest pieces of evidence for the relation between disorganization and susceptibility to carcinogenesis is the fact that dissociated cells can be more readily transformed in vitro [in a test tube or petri dish] than the same cell type in vivo [in the body]." Tsonis, 621.
34.   Rubin, 2939.
35.   Ibid., 2937.
36.   "A dedifferentiated cell is a cell devoid of tissue-specific characteristics. Cells of the early embryo (before determination) are dedifferentiated. Cancer cells do not show the

characteristics of the tissue of their origin. In this respect cancer cells resemble embryonic cells." Tsonis, 617.

37.   "In the slender microscopic form of *C. Elegans*—a round-worm so small it takes just three days to develop into a full-grown adult—scientists may have stumbled onto a clue to the mystery of why diseases like Alzheimer's suddenly cause massive numbers of brain cells to die. In the current issue of the journal *Nature*, Columbia University Researchers Martin Chalfie and Eve Wolinksy report that after studying a similar wave of cell death in the *C. Elegans* roundworm they have identified three defective genes as the culprit. Roundworms are not humans, of course. But they are the best surrogate researchers have, because the kind of close observation and targeted researchers needed to find the defective genes are not possible on anything more complicated than a round-worm. There are good reasons to believe that, on a molecular level, *C. Elegans* may serve a very useful analogy for what goes on in a human brain. For example, humans and the worm share many of the same neurotransmitters as well as many similar neurological genes and proteins. Armed with a profile of the defective genes, the two scientists hope that eventually they will be able to look for similar defective genes in humans and perhaps design diagnostic tests to detect their presence and identify those at risk for neurodegenerative diseases like Alzheimer's or Huntington's diseases. In the meantime, the roundworms will be used as models to better understand neurodegenerative diseases and test new therapies that might help prevent cell death." M. Gladwell, "Genetic Alzheimer's clue in worms," *Washington Post* (June 4, 1990).

38.   "Already a century ago, pathologists considered cancer cells as 'undifferentiated' or 'poorly differentiated,' and it was frequently admitted that there was a relationship between differentiation and tumorigenicity: the less differentiated the morphology of a tumour cell, the more malignant it was considered. Only in recent years, however, has an increasing body of evidence led to the view that malignancy is a disorder of cell differentiation." Jacob, 4.

39.   Farber, "Pre-cancerous steps," 177.

40.   J. V. Schwind, "Cancer: Regressive evolution?" *Oncology* 29 (1974): 174.

41.   Ibid.

42.   Witkin, 100.

43. Herrlich, 500.
44. L. M. Field et al., "Molecular evidence that insecticide resistance in peach-potato aphids (Myzus persicae Sulz.) results from amplification of an esterase gene," *Biochemistry Journal* (April 1988): 309–12.
45. G. K. Scott et al., "Differential amplification of antifreeze protein genes in the pleuronectinae, *Journal of Molecular Evolution* (1988): 29–35.
46. Farber, "Pre-cancerous steps," 176.
47. Rubin, 2937.
48. Ibid.
49. "As development proceeds, the competence of tissues to change from one differentiative fate to another by altering the environment of the tissue is gradually reduced but not lost completely." Rubin refers in this quote to embryonic cells, and he's referring to differentiation, not dedifferentiation, but the principle probably applies to cancer cells as well. Ibid., 2939, emphasis added.
50. See Leon Glass and Michael C. Mackey, *From Clocks to Chaos: The Rhythms of Life* (Princeton, NJ: Princeton Univ. Press, 1988), 90.
51. See, for example, S. Saracco et al., "Spontaneously regressing adrenocortical carcinoma in a newborn," *Cancer* 62 (August 1988): 507–11. Also N. L. Carlsen, "How frequent is the spontaneous remission of neuroblastomas?" *British Journal of Cancer* 61 (March 1990): 441–46.
52. B. E. Johnson et al., "myc family oncogene amplification in tumor cell lines established from small cell lung cancer patients and its relationship to clinical status and course," *Journal of Clinical Investigations* 79 (June 1987): 1629.
53. N. V. Levina, "Chromosomes and drug resistance of tumors," *Eksperimentalnaia Onkologiia* 6 (1984): 14–19. Quote taken from the English abstract.
54. "One can consider amplification of drug resistance genes and oncogenes as analogous processes." Schimke, 1913.
55. J. J. McCormack, "Dihydrofolate reductase inhibitors as potential drugs," *Medicinal Research Reviews* 1 (1981): 315. Also, "Multidrug-resistant (MDR) cells demonstrate the increase activity of the membrane transport system performing efflux of diverse lipophilic drugs and fluorescent dyes from the cells." A. A. Neyfakh et al., "Multidrug-resistance phenotype of a subpopulation of T-lymphocytes without drug selection,"

Experimental Cell Research 185 (December 1989): 496.
56.   P. Volling et al., "Oncogenes in squamous epithelial cancers in the area of the head and neck" (in German), *Laryngologie, Rhinologie, Otologie* (April 1988): 160–64. Quote taken from the English abstract.
57.   R. Seshadrai et al., "N-myc amplified in retinoblastoma cell line FMC-RB1," *Cancer Genetics and Cytogenetics* (July 1988): 25.
58.   J. J. Varley et al., "Alterations to either c-erbB-2 (neu) or c-myc protooncogenes in breast carcinomas correlate with poor short-term prognosis," *Oncogene* 1 (1987): 423.
59.   Wrynn Smith, *Cancer: A Profile of Health and Disease in America* (New York: Facts on File Publications, 1987), 9.
60.   Committee on Labor and Public Welfare, United States Senate, *Conquest of Cancer* (Brief Summary and Bill Text of S. 34) (Washington, DC: U.S. Government Printing Office, 1971).
61.   R. K. Oldham, "Biotherapy: General principles," in R. K. Oldham, ed., *Principles of Cancer Biotherapy* (New York: Raven Press, 1987), 3.
62.   Smith, 2.
63.   J. Gross, "Emotional expression in cancer onset and progression," *Social Science and Medicine* 28 (1989): 1239–48.
64.   Rubin, 2940, emphasis added.

Chapter 6
How Shall We Know the Truth?

1.   See Thomas Kuhn, *The Structure of Scientific Revolutions,* 2d ed. (Chicago: Univ. of Chicago Press, 1970).
2.   F. Bacon, "Novum Organum," in R. M. Hutchins et al., eds., *Great Books of the Western World,* 54 vols., (Chicago: Encyclopaedia Britannica, 1952), 30:107.
3.   Ibid.
4.   Ibid., 105.
5.   Ibid., 108.
6.   Ibid.
7.   Ibid., 107.
8.   Ibid., 108.
9.   R. Descartes, "Discourse on the method of rightly conducting the reason and seeking for truth in the sciences," in R. M. Hutchins et al., eds., *Great Books of the Western World,* 54

vols., (Chicago: Encyclopaedia Britannica, 1952), 31:42.
10. Descartes, 44.
11. Ibid.
12. Ibid., 62.
13. Ibid., 61.
14. I. Prigogine and I. Stengers, *Order out of Chaos: Man's New Dialogue with Nature* (New York: Bantam Books, 1984), 41, emphasis added.
15. I modified Haken's quote slightly to make it read more smoothly. H. Haken, "Operational approaches to complex systems: An introduction," in H. Haken, ed., *Complex Systems–Operational Approaches* (Berlin: Springer-Verlag, 1985), 1.
16. "This view rests on the argument that science is analysis and analysis requires the resolution of a subject into its simplest elements. Such a procedure generates a scheme that relates the sciences to each other. Within this scheme, the laws that govern crowds, classes of persons, and societies are based on the qualities and characteristics of the individual. The causes of an individual's actions arise from anatomy, physiology, and the biochemistry of brain mechanisms. These subjects are in turn resolvable to the laws of chemistry and physics. This process of analysis finally stops with high-energy physics, which studies the ultimate particles." Robert Augros and George Stanciu, *The New Biology: Discovering the Wisdom in Nature* (Boston: New Science Library, 1987), 5.
17. "Science strives to reduce our experience to symbols. Experiences are colorful, multi-faceted, and fuzzy along the edges; symbols are bland, one-dimensional, and precisely-bounded. Real world observations can be bulky and ill-shaped and can have both strong and tenuous ties with a myriad of other real world observations; abstractions are built of simple, smooth-faced elements, uncoupled from other constructs. . . . Scientifically, we give up the shifting and elusive mystery of the world, but, in exchange, we gain the standardized and reproducible abstractions from which we can build precise determinate explanations." Michael J. Katz, *Templets and the Explanation of Complex Patterns* (Cambridge, England: Cambridge Univ. Press, 1986), 85.
18. J. Von Neumann, cited in Roberto Serra, Massimo Andretta, and Mario Compiani, *Introduction to the Physics of Complex Systems: The Mesoscopic Approach to Fluctuations, Nonlinearity, and Self-organization* (Oxford: Pergamon Press, 1986), xvii.

19.   Katz, 19, 5.
20.   "Let me list the elements of such a revolutionary approach.
      First, isolating a few quantities, after the observation these
      can be treated as numbers and hence related mathematical-
      ly, with the framework of a suitable calculus. Second, these
      few elements can be organized into a simple experiment
      which can be verified anywhere. The criterion of truth . . . is
      related only to the experimental verification." F. T. Arecchi,
      "Foreword," in Serra, Andretta, and Compiani, vii.
21.   Katz, 85.
22.   In contrast, a medical doctor writing to the *Journal of the
      American Medical Association* complains as follows about the
      judge who convicted the AMA of conspiracy to destroy the
      profession of chiropractic: "She [Judge Getzendanner] does
      not see that a therapeutic maneuver can be effective without
      having scientific merit." C. F. Needles, Letter to the Editor,
      Journal of the American Medical Association 259 (May 13, 1988):
      2694.
23.   I. R. Epstein, "Chemical oscillations and nonlinear chemical
      dynamics," in Erica Jen, ed., *1989 Lectures in Complex Systems*
      (Redwood City, CA: Addison Wesley Publishing Company,
      1990), 247.
24.   C. Sparrow, *The Lorenz Equations: Bifurcations, Chaos, and
      Strange Attractors* (New York: Springer-Verlag New York,
      1982), 6.
25.   F. Moon, *Chaotic Vibrations for Applied Scientists and Engineers*
      (New York: John Wiley & Sons, 1987), 6, emphasis added.
26.   S. Lundqvist et al., eds., *Order and Chaos in Nonlinear Physical
      Systems* (New York: Plenum Press, 1988), 183.
27.   H. L. Swinney, "Observations of order and chaos in non-
      linear systems," in D. Campbell et al., eds., *Order in Chaos*
      (Amsterdam: North Holland Publishing Company, 1983),
      12.
28.   B. V. Mandelbrot, *The Fractal Geometry of Nature* (San Fran-
      cisco: W. H. Freeman and Company, 1983), 22.
29.   B. Mandelbrot, "How long is the coast of Britain?" *Science*
      156 (1967): 636–38.
30.   Cited in Mandelbrot, *The Fractal Geometry of Nature*, 7.
31.   Cited in ibid., 8.
32.   B. J. West et al., "Physiology in fractal dimensions," *American
      Scientist* 75 (July-August 1987): 355.
33.   Ibid.

34. Although the graphic designers at Lucasfilms developed their techniques from Mandelbrot's work, Mandelbrot considers that they do not generate "proper" fractals. The issue became serious enough to warrant articles in the journal *Communications of the Association of Computing Machinery.* See the discussion in M. Batty, "Fractals—Geometry between dimensions," *New Scientist* (April 4, 1985): 31, 34.

35. Quantum theory also attacked the notion of absolute measurement with Heisenberg's "uncertainty principle." However, Heisenberg's principle simply suggests that we must be satisfied in certain instances with statistical averages. It doesn't undermine the more fundamental assumption of continuity, as Mandelbrot does. As Max Planck says, "It should first be observed that the validity of statistical laws is entirely compatible with a strict causality." M. Planck, "Physics and world philosophy," in J. H. Weaver, ed., *The World of Physics: A Small Library of the Literature of Physics from Antiquity to the Present,* 3 vols. (New York: Simon and Schuster, 1987), 3:708.

36. See, for example, "Notes from the underground: Testing the effects of prolonged isolation," *Newsweek* 113 (July 5, 1989): 64.

37. "When entrained to 24 h[ours], all circadian rhythms keep distinct phase-relationship to each other, representing a high degree of temporal order." Jurgen Aschoff, "Temporal orientation: Circadian clocks in animals and humans," *Animal Behaviour* 37 (1989): 892–93, see also 888–90.

38. "The specific relation between the macroscopic and microscopic level is established and derived in synergetics [Haken's name for contextual science] by means of two concepts, mainly that of the order parameters and the slaving principle. The order parameters are the macroscopic observables, which describe the macroscopic behavior of the system. According to the slaving principle, once the macroscopic observables are given the behavior of the microscopic elements is determined. In this way an enormous reduction of the degrees of freedom is achieved, namely in a laser there may be 10^{16} degrees of freedom of the atoms and 1 degree of freedom of the field mode. Due to the slaving principle at the lasing threshold, the whole system is governed by a single degree of freedom." H. Haken, "Operational approaches to complex systems: An introduction," in H. Haken, ed., *Complex Systems—Operational Approaches* (Berlin: Springer-Verlag, 1985), 4–5. Erica Jen describes the subject matter of contextual science

as "systems that exhibit complicated behavior but for which there is some hope that the underlying structure is simple in the sense of being governed by a small number of degrees of freedom." E. Jen, "Preface," in Erica Jen, ed., *1989 Lectures in Complex Systems* (Redwood City, CA: Addison Wesley Publishing Company, 1990), xiv.

39. Sparrow, 6.
40. Mandelbrot, *The Fractal Geometry of Nature*, 22.
41. "The eye sometimes sees spurious relationships which statistical analysis later negates, but this problem arises mostly in areas of science where samples are small. In the areas we shall explore, samples are huge." Ibid.
42. Bacon, 30:105.
43. Ibid.
44. Robert B. Livingston speaks of Descartes' "philosophy of universal doubt" and points out that it was entirely based on the proposition that "perceptions can be subject to error." R. B. Livingston, "Sensory processing, perception, and behavior," in Robert G. Grenell and Sabit Gabay, eds., *Biological Foundations of Psychiatry*, 2 vols. (New York: Raven Press, 1976), 1:65.
45. Cited in Prigogine and Stengers, 35.

Chapter 7
Contextual Healing's Challenge to Medicine

1. In one instance, research exposed cells to chemotherapy and saw a 250- to 350-fold amplification of the genes in question. B. J. Maurer et al., "Novel submicroscopic extrachromosomal elements containing amplified genes in human cells," *Nature* 327 (June 1987): 434–37. When drugs are combined, gene amplification "is far greater (100 times) than predicted from the frequencies as determined separately for each drug." R. T. Schimke, "Methotrexate resistance and gene amplification: Mechanisms and implications," *Cancer* 57 (May 1986): 1913.
2. "One can consider amplification of drug resistance genes and oncogenes as analogous processes to overcome growth constraints of cells; in one case the 'constraint' is that imposed by the oncologist, whereas in the other the constraint is that imposed in vivo. . . . In terms of solid tumors . . . those tumors that result in death are those that are [called] aneu-

ploid. . . . Might [chemotherapy] treatments convert relatively benign tumors into a state of aneuploidy and progression to a more lethal form? Indeed, treatment of an experimental tumor with cancer chemotherapeutic agents has been shown to increase heterogeneity in DNA/cell [a sign of aneuploidy]." Ibid., 1913, 1915. Other researchers have associated gene amplification with "shortened survival." B. E. Johnson et al., "myc-family oncogene amplification in tumor cell lines established from small cell lung cancer patients and its relationship to clinical status and course," *Journal of Clinical Investigations* 79 (June 1987): 1629.

3. Cited in J. Silberner, "Resisting cancer chemotherapy," *Science News* 131 (January 3, 1987): 13.

4. "Feedback and feedforward mechanisms [occur when] metabolites act directly as signals in the control of their own breakdown or biosynthesis. Feedback is negative or positive. Negative feedback results in inhibition of the activity or synthesis of an enzyme or several enzymes in a reaction chain by the endproduct. Inhibition of the synthesis of an enzyme is called enzyme repression. . . . This type of feedback control is well known for amino acid biosynthesis in prokaryotic organisms, and is variously known as endproduct inhibition, feedback inhibition, and retroinhibition. In positive feedback, or feedback activation, an endproduct activates an enzyme responsible for its own production." "Metabolic control," in Thomas Scott and Mary Eagleson, *Concise Encyclopedia of Biochemistry* (Berlin: Walter de Gruyter, 1988), 367.

5. "The endproduct may also regulate its own synthesis by actually inhibiting the synthetic process, so that the rate of production of endproduct is finely adjusted to its rate of utilization by the cell." Ibid.

6. "Searching for a better clot buster," *Science News* 133 (April 9, 1988): 230.

7. R. J. Cody, "Renin system activity as a determinant of response to treatment in hypertension and heart failure," *Hypertension* 5 (September-October 1983): 36–42.

8. "Enzymes, like all catalysts, accelerate reactions but cannot alter the position of equilibrium." Franklin M. Harold, *The Vital Force: A Study of Bioenergetics* (New York: W. H. Freeman and Company, 1986), 31.

9. Cited in Jeff Goldberg, *Anatomy of a Scientific Discovery* (New

York: Bantam Books, 1988), 128.

10. A. R. D. Stebbing, "Hormesis—The stimulation of growth by low levels of inhibitors," *The Science of the Total Environment* 22 (1983): 216.

11. L. A. Sagan, "On radiation, paradigms, and hormesis," *Science* 245 (August 11, 1989): 374.

12. "Haseman reviewed all of the 2-y cancer bioassay feeding studies conducted in Fisher 344 rats in the National Toxicology Program. There was a total of 25 studies, each with a control and two exposure levels. Many of the agents are now regulated as carcinogens. Dr. Haseman's analysis of the data revealed that there were as many significant decreases in organ-specific cancers as there were increases. On the basis of these studies, it would have been equally logical to focus on the significant deficits of some site-specific cancers, with the conclusion that the agents are useful in protection against cancer. Haseman also found that the exposed animals had statistically greater survival in these studies than did the control animals." L. A. Sagan, "What is hormesis and why haven't we heard about it before," *Health Physics* 52 (May 1987): 521.

13. Stebbing. The phrase appears in the title of his article.

14. E. J. Calabrese et al., "The occurrence of chemically induced hormesis," *Health Physics* 52 (May 1987): 531, 534.

15. Stebbing, 214.

16. Sagan, "What is hormesis . . . ?" 12.

17. Stebbing, 227.

18. S. Wolfe, "Are radiation-induced effects hormetic?" *Science* 245 (August 11, 1989): 575.

19. Stebbing, 228.

20. Ibid.

21. Ibid., 229. Stebbing does suggest the feedback explanation. "The more frequent type of control mechanism for regulating biosynthetic pathways is end product inhibition. Control is achieved by the end product of a pathway which inhibits the action of an allosteric enzyme catalyzing an earlier reaction in the same pathway. . . . The response of any control mechanism operating in this way is non-specific and counter-action will occur whatever the cause of inhibition."

22. A. R. D. Stebbing, "Growth hormesis: A by-product of control," *Health Physics* 52 (May 1987): 543.

23. A. Furst, "Hormetic effects in pharmacology: Pharmacological

inversions as prototypes for hormesis," *Health Physics* 52 (May 1987): 527.

24. Silberner, 13.

25. "Searching for a better clot buster," 230.

26. " 'With interferon we learned a lesson,' says Hilton Levy, head of the molecular virology section of the National Institute of Allergy and Infectious Disease (NIAID) at the Frederick (Md.) Cancer Research Facility. 'We thought it would be the wonder drug and were shocked when it wasn't.' ... Part of the problem with interferon injections, Levy says, is that mixtures of alpha, beta, and gamma interferons are probably necessary for the substance to have any effect in a given disease or tumor state. 'There are 16 different types of alpha interferon alone,' he says, 'each of which has different biological activity.' The tricky part is knowing which particular interferons are needed for which diseases." D. W. Bennett, "Drugs that fight cancer ... naturally," *Science News* 128 (July 27, 1985): 58.

27. J. W. Mold et al., "The cascade effect in the clinical care of patients," *New England Journal of Medicine* 314 (February 20, 1986): 512.

28. S. G. Seckler et al., "Disseminated disease of medicine," *Archives of Internal Medicine* 117 (March 1966): 448.

29. Contextual healers must also realize that negative feedback affects them as they seek to use druglike herbs. The Chinese, for example, acknowledge three distinct classes of herbs: toxic herbs, moderately toxic herbs, and nontoxic herbs. They're also called poison herbs, medicinal herbs, and food herbs. Poison herbs (used therapeutically) have an immediate beneficial effect followed by a rapid decline, so they're used very carefully and very short term. Medicinal herbs may be used longer because both their benefits and the decline they eventually provoke take longer to develop. Food herbs may literally be eaten as foods because they have only a long-term beneficial effect, with no decline. Only the food herbs are contextual. Poison herbs and medicinal herbs contain druglike substances that replace or block body chemicals and therefore provoke a negative-feedback reversing as readily as the purified drugs of Western medicine. See the discussion in R. C. Crozier, *Traditional Medicine in Modern China* (Cambridge, MA: Harvard Univ. Press, 1968), 19–20. Also Steven Fulder, *The Tao of Medicine: Oriental Remedies and the Phar-*

macology of Harmony (New York: Harper & Row, 1987).

30. R. K. Oldham, "Biotherapy: General principles," in R. K. Oldham, ed., *Principles of Cancer Biotherapy* (New York: Raven Press, 1987), 1.

31. Ibid.

32. M. Gladwell, "Serious side effects linked to many approved drugs," *Washington Post*, May 28, 1990.

33. M. S. Kramer et al., "Adverse drug reactions in general pediatric outpatients," *Journal of Pediatrics* 106 (February 1985): 305–10.

34. Eric W. Martin, *Hazards of Medication* (Philadelphia: J. B. Lippincott Company, 1978): 1.

35. K. Steel et al., "Iatrogenic illness on a general medical service at a university hospital," *New England Journal of Medicine* (March 12, 1981): 638–42.

36. An article published in the *Journal of the American Medical Association* reports an even higher figure–2.5 percent–although it applies to intensive care units where patients may be at greater risk. P. Trunet et al., "The role of iatrogenic disease in admissions to intensive care," *Journal of the American Medical Association* 244 (December 12, 1980): 2617–20.

37. Cited in J. Beck, "Treatment standards are on the way," *Ogden [Utah] Standard-Examiner* (February 6, 1989).

38. Testimony by Dr. Robert M. Centor, Hearing before the Subcommittee on Health and the Environment of the Committee on Energy and Commerce, House of Representatives, One Hundred First Congress, First Session, on H.R. 2601, June 16, 1989, 64.

39. Ibid.

40. M. N. G. Dukes, ed., *Side Effects of Drugs Annual I: A Worldwide Yearly Survey of New Data and Trends* (Amsterdam: Excerpta Medica, 1977), viii.

41. Cited in P. Bunker, "Is efficacy the gold standard for quality assessment?" *Inquiry* 25 (Spring 1988): 52.

42. R. L. Engler et al., "Misrepresentation and responsibility in medical research," *New England Journal of Medicine* 317 (November 26, 1987): 1383–89.

43. B. Rensberger, "Harvard researchers retract published medical 'discovery'," *Washington Post* (November 22, 1986).

44. "Trouble at Stanford," *Washington Post* (December 6, 1988).

45. P. W. Valentine, "Drug researcher sentenced for academic fraud," *Washington Post* (November 11, 1988).

46. D. S. Greenberg, "Lab-scam: How science goes bad," *Washington Post* (April 24, 1988).
47. Engler, 1385.
48. Ibid.
49. Ibid.
50. Ibid.
51. Ibid.
52. L. Eisenberg, "Science in medicine: Too much or too little and too limited in scope?" *The American Journal of Medicine* 84 (March 1988): 485.
53. Cited in Beck.
54. D. M. Berwick, "Health services research and quality of care: Assignments for the 1990s," *Medical Care* 27 (August 1989): 765.
55. Hearing, 64.
56. Testimony by James O. Mason, Assistant Secretary for Health, Public Health Service, Department of Health and Human Services. Hearing, 43.
57. Eisenberg, 484.
58. Testimony by Constance Winslow, who participated in the RAND study. Hearing, June 16, 1989, 78.
59. J. E. Wennberg, "The paradox of appropriate care," *Journal of the American Medical Association* 258 (November 13, 1987): 2568.
60. Bunker, 53.
61. Cited in Beck.
62. Hearing, June 16, 1989, 43.
63. For references to the quotes in this section, see chapter 6, pages 102–3.

Chapter 8
Contextual Healing's Challenge to Our Lawmakers

1. Cited in Franklin M. Harold, *The Vital Force: A Study of Bioenergetics* (New York: W. H. Freeman and Company, 1986), xi.
2. See G. Kocher, "Amish boy's illness argued in court," *News-Enterprise* (Elizabeth, Kentucky), January 27, 1989.
3. As I mentioned in footnote 29 of chapter 7, herbs aren't necessarily a contextual therapy. Medicinal herbs contain drug-like substances that control the body as directly as medical drugs do, although their wholeness may moderate their ef-

fects. Other herbs, however, are nutritional, and therefore contextual, meaning that they sustain the operations of the genes without overruling them. The Chinese have long distinguished between medicinal herbs and food herbs, and I would probably rely most strongly on Chinese food herbs. For a discussion of medicinal herbs and food herbs, see R. C. Crozier, *Traditional Medicine in Modern China* (Cambridge, MA: Harvard Univ. Press, 1968), 19–20. For a comprehensive treatment of the entire Chinese herbal philosophy, see Yanchi Liu, *The Essential Book of Traditional Chinese Medicine, Volume 1: Theory* (New York: Columbia Univ. Press, 1988).

4. Utah Code Anno. 78-3A(2)(17)(C).
5. U.S. Congress, Office of Technology Assessment, *Unconventional Cancer Treatments*, OTA-H-405 (Washington, DC: U.S. Government Printing Office, 1990), 200, emphasis added.
6. See note 3.
7. Y. Sun et al., "Immune restoration and/or augmentation of local graft versus host reaction by traditional Chinese medicinal herbs," *Cancer* 52 (July 1, 1983): 70–73.
8. The Director at that time was David Robinson.
9. "Although requirements vary among States, in general, a person must be a graduate of an accredited medical school, have completed 1 year of residency training in a program approved by the Accreditation Council for Graduate Medical Education, and have passed the Federation Licensing Examination sponsored by the Federation of State Medical Boards." *Unconventional Cancer Treatments*, 214.
10. Ibid., 213.
11. Ibid.
12. The spokesperson asked that I not mention his company's name.
13. Apparently natural products can be covered by certain "use patents," and the extraction process itself may be patentable. I don't understand patent law, however, and can't comment on the accuracy of this part of the representative's statement. For a more complete discussion of the problem of patenting natural products, see S. L. DeFelice, *From Oysters to Insulin: Nature & Medicine at Odds* (Seacaucus, NJ: Citadel Press, 1986).
14. Steven N. Wiggins, *The Cost of Developing a New Drug* (Washington, DC: Pharmaceutical Manufacturers Association, 1987). The Pharmaceutical Manufacturers Association funded the

study, Dr. Wiggins reports.

15. The FDA spokesperson I spoke with was press officer Bill Griggs.

16. The Wiggins reports itself confirms that the $125 million includes $60 million of opportunity costs, or the cost of tying up money that might be used for other purposes. Wiggins, iv.

17. Ibid., 1.

18. The specialist I spoke with was Paula Botstein.

19. T. Friend, "Cancer fraud lures thousands," *USA Today* (March 17, 1988). By stating that "the vast majority of the purveyors of quack [unapproved] products are gangsters," Norris left open the possibility that a few are not. However, the tone of his remarks effectively condemned anyone selling products the FDA hasn't approved.

20. "There are, in general, no legal restrictions on a U.S. patient's right to choose a treatment for himself or herself, either in the United States or in foreign countries (although parents choosing treatment for a child may be restricted by legal precedents). However, some treatments are excluded from choice in the United States because they involve the use of unapproved substances that could only be offered illegally here." *Unconventional Cancer Treatments,* 6. Also, contextual healers also suffer from the fact that both government and private insurance companies refuse to pay for therapies that fall outside mainstream medical practice. "Insurers tend to stipulate that coverage of medical treatments is dependent on the treatment's being 'reasonable and necessary,' or 'medically necessary.' Generally, to fulfill these terms the treatment must be accepted as effective and safe. Medicare, for instance, reasons that if the treatment is not accepted (by the medical profession) as effective then it is not reasonable to use the treatment. Third-party payers treat most unconventional cancer treatments as not having been shown to be medically efficacious in the treatment of cancer." Ibid., 175.

21. Ilya Prigogine, *From Being to Becoming* (San Francisco: W. H. Freeman, 1980), xxvii.

22. M. A. B. Brazier, *A History of Neurophysiology in the 19th Century* (New York: Raven Press, 1988), 42.

23. *Unconventional Cancer Treatments,* 6.

24. Ibid.

25. Ibid.

26.   W. T. Jarvis, "Chiropractic: A challenge for health educa-
       tion," *Journal of School Health* (April 1974): 213.
27.   *Unconventional Cancer Treatments,* 5.
28.   United States v. Articles of Food and Drug, 372 F.Supp. 915,
       920–921 (N.D. Ga. 1974).
29.   From H.R. 3562 (3)(B)(i).
30.   See the statement, for example, in Christopher Collier and
       James Lincoln Collier, *Decision in Philadelphia: The Constitu-
       tional Convention of 1787* (New York: Ballantine Books, 1987),
       285–86.
31.   Johnson and Graham's Lessee v. William M'Intosh, 21 U.S.
       543, 572 (1823).
32.   Rhode Island v. Massachusetts, 39 U.S. 210, 225 (1840).
33.   Hopt v. Utah, 120 U.S. 430, 439 (1887).
34.   Thomas Jefferson, letter to William Charles Jarvis, Septem-
       ber 28, 1820, *Presidential Papers of Thomas Jefferson,* Library of
       Congress, Washington, D.C. (1944), microfilm series I:1820-22.
35.   Cited in Charles Medawar, "On our side of the fence," in M.
       N. G. Dukes and L. Beely, eds., *Side Effects of Drugs Annual
       13* (Amsterdam: Elsevier, 1989), xxviii.

Chapter 9
Contextual Healing's Challenge to Each of Us

1.   Eric Partridge, *Origins: A Short Etymological Dictionary of
       Modern English* (New York: Macmillan Publishing Company,
       1966), 677.
2.   Steven Jay Gould, *The Panda's Thumb: More Reflections on
       Natural History* (London: W. W. Norton, 1980), 95–107.
3.   In fact, the "treasure" in the common myth is a very specific
       understanding, which Campbell describes in these words:
       "The perilous journey was a labor not of attainment but of
       reattainment, not discovery but rediscovery. The godly powers
       sought and dangerously won are revealed to have been within
       the heart of the hero all the time. He is 'the king's son' who
       has come to know who he is and therewith has entered into
       the exercise of his proper power—'God's son,' who has
       learned to know how much that title means. From this point
       of view the hero is symbolical of that divine creative and
       redemptive image which is hidden within us all, only waiting
       to be known and rendered into life." Joseph Campbell, *The
       Hero with a Thousand Faces* (Princeton, NJ: Princeton Univ.

Press, 1968), 39.
4. King James translation.
5. Partridge, 148.
6. See the discussion in chapter 8, pages 156–57.
7. *The Daily Herald* (Provo, Utah; January 31, 1989): 1.
8. Ibid., 1–2.
9. "The legitimate object of government is 'to do for the people
    what needs to be done, but which they can not, by individual
    effort, do at all, or do so well, by themselves.' There are many
    such things—some of them exist independently of the injus-
    tice in the world. Making and maintaining roads, bridges,
    and the like; providing for the helpless, young, and afflicted;
    common schools; and disposing of deceased mens' property,
    are instances. But a far larger class of objects springs from
    the injustice of men. If one people will make war upon
    another, it is a necessity . . . to unite and cooperate for
    defense. Hence, the military department. If some men kill,
    or beat, or constrain others, or despoil them of property by
    force, fraud, or noncompliance with contracts, it is a com-
    mon object with peaceful and just men to prevent it. Hence
    the criminal and civil departments." Abraham Lincoln, *The
    Collected Works of Abraham Lincoln,* ed. Roy P. Basler, 8 vols.
    (New Brunswick, NJ: Rutgers Univ. Press, 1953), 2:221–22.
10. W. H. Romme et al., "Historical perspective on the Yel-
    lowstone fires of 1988," *Bioscience* 89 (November 1989): 696.
11. Ibid., 698.
12. *Newsweek* (October 25, 1982): 111.

Chapter 10
Finding the Will to Change

1. Hearing before the Subcommittee on Health and the En-
    vironment of the Committee on Energy and Commerce,
    House of Representatives, One Hundred First Congress,
    First Session, on H.R. 2601, June 16, 1989, 77.
2   D. M. Berwick, "Health services research and quality of care:
    Assignments for the 1990s," *Medical Care* 27 (August 1989):
    764.
3. Testimony by Dr. Uwe Reinhardt, president-elect of the
    Association for Health Services Research, in Hearing, 64.
4. Berwick, 764.
5. A. R. Tarlov, "The rising supply of physicians and the pursuit

of better health," *Journal of Medical Education* 3 (February 1988): 99.

6.   J. Beck, "Treatment standards are on the way," *Ogden [Utah] Standard Examiner* (February 6, 1989).

7.   N. E. Davies et al., "Applying brakes to the runaway American health care system," *Journal of the American Medical Association* 263 (January 5, 1990): 73.

8.   "The most dramatic instance of business concern has been the proposal of large employers in Arizona for a constitutional amendment aimed at placing the health care sector under a public-utility system of control." Eli Ginzberg, *The Medical Triangle: Physicians, Politicians, and the Public* (Cambridge, MA: Harvard Univ. Press, 1990), 26.

9.   A. Enthoven et al., "A consumer-choice health plan for the 1990s: Universal health insurance in a system designed to promote quality and economy," *New England Journal of Medicine* 320 (January 5, 1990): 29–37 (part 1) and (January 12, 1990): 94–101 (part 2).

10. "What, then, must our nation do? The answer seems simple enough. . . . We must ration health care." Davies.

11. D. M. Berwick speaks of "revenue and income caps" and "assaults on physician income." Berwick, 764.

12. J. H. Knowles, "Introduction," in John H. Knowles, ed., *Doing Better and Feeling Worse: Health in the United States* (New York: W. W. Norton, 1977), 5. Also, "Any rational observer of the scientific foundations for clinical practice must conclude that our society has seriously underinvested in the systematic study of the technologies used in health care." Berwick, 765.

13. Ibid., 768.

14. Knowles, 4.

15. Ibid.

16. L. Thomas, "On the science and technology of medicine," in Knowles, 46.

Index

E

F

G

H

I

K

L

M

Mandelbrot, Benoit – 114–17, 120
  See also Fractal geometry
Mast, Danny – 143–44, 164, 171
McClintock, Barbara – 53
Mechanism
  See Classical science, principles of
Medical review boards
  See Government regulation of health care
Medicine
  Cascade effect – 132
  Costs of medical care – 37, 147–48, 177–78
  Double-blind experimental design – 109–10, 143
  Goals of – 20, 36–37, 101
  Incompleteness of – 4, 124, 128, 140–42
  Lack of practice standards – 139–40
  Medical research, fraudulent – 136–37
  Medical research, quality of – 135–36
  Microscopic focus – 19–21
  Molecular emphasis – 18–20, 29–30, 36–37, 85–87, 108–10
  Practical monopoly of – 2, 151
  Side effects – 98–99, 124–26, 132–34
  See also Classical science
Memories, working – 75–77, 80–82
  See also Context parameters, Mind
Mickey Mouse, example of – 165
Model building
  See Classical science, principles of

N

National Council Against Health Fraud – 57, 155
Negative feedback
  See Contextual science, principles of
Newton, Isaac – 2, 28, 30–34, 39, 41, 106, 115, 137
Nicolis, Gregoire – 12–14, 49
Norris, John – 150

O

Office of Technology Assessment
  See Government regulation of health care

P

Parents' rights
    See Government regulation of health care
Peptic ulcer – 24–25
Perrin, Jean – 116
Pfluger, Eduoard – 34
Pharmaceutical Manufacturers Association – 147–48
Physis – 27–28
Poincarè, Henri – 39–42, 44–45, 106
Premenstrual syndrome (PMS) – 11, 36, 56
Pribram, Karl – 77
Prigogine, Ilya – 12–14, 18, 21, 41, 49, 57, 89, 151–52
Product labeling laws
    See Government regulation of health care

Q

Quantum theory – 41

R

Rationality
    See Classical science, principles of
Reductionism
    See Classical science, principles of
Reproducibility
    See Contextual science, principles of
Rhythm
    See Contextual science, principles of
Rubin, Harry – 56, 92–93, 97, 100
Rush, Benjamin – 30
Russell, John Scott – 58–59

S

Schimke, Robert T. – 93, 99, 124
Schwann, Theodor – 91–92
Self-organization
    See Contextual science, principles of
Shannon, Claude – 67
Slaving principle
    See Contextual science, principles of
Slime mold – 51

About the Author

Dean Black received a Ph.D. degree from
Pennsylvania State University and is listed in
American Men and Women of Science. He has
taught at the University of Southern California
and Brigham Young University and currently
writes and lectures on topics related to contextual healing and philosophies of living.

For information about additional Tapestry Press products by Dean Black, call toll free, 1-800-333-4290